PEARSON SCIENCE 6–8

SASKATCHEWAN EDITION

Program Overview

PEARSON

Pearson Science 6–8, Program Overview, Saskatchewan Edition was published previously as *Pearson Saskatchewan Science 6–8, Program Overview.*

Customer Service
Pearson Canada Inc.
26 Prince Andrew Place
Don Mills, ON
M3C 2T8

ISBN: 978-0-13-312730-0

The development team wishes to thank:
Dr. Glen S. Aikenhead
Judy Bear, Traditional Knowledge Keeper, Sweetgrass First Nation
Dr. Herman Michell
Rhonda Phillips
Ted View
The Saskatchewan Ministry of Education

Publisher: Reid McAlpine
Research and Communications Manager: Martin Goldberg
Managing Editor: Lee Ensor
Developmental Editor: Eileen Pyne-Rudzik, Ph.D.
Editorial Assistants: Marissa Murray, Kristiana Shin
Copy Editor: Ruth Peckover
Production Coordinator: Louise Avery
Cover Design: David Cheung
Interior Design: Carolyn E. Sebestyen
Text Composition: Computer Composition of Canada Inc.
Illustrations: Computer Composition of Canada Inc.
Vice-President, Publishing: Mark Cobham

8 18

Printed and bound in Canada

PEARSON

www.pearsoncanada.ca

Program Overview

Table of Contents

1. Using the *Pearson Science Program* in Your Classroom

2. Assessment and Evaluation

3. Fostering Scientific Knowledge

4. Helping Students Relate Science and Technology to the World Outside the School

5. Encouraging Responsible Attitudes in Science (includes Safety section)

6. Generic Line Masters

7. CD-ROM

1 Using the *Pearson Science Program* in Your Classroom

Using the *Pearson Science 6 Teacher's Resource*

Note: Any references to *Pearson Science* resources in this document are to the Saskatchewan Edition.

Pearson Science 6 Teacher's Resource provides all of the tools you need to implement the *Pearson Science 6* program. Information to help you plan each unit before you start includes:

- A Unit Indicators Correlation Chart lists indicators within unit outcomes, including references to specific lessons that the indicators are covered in. Opportunities for ongoing assessment are listed to prepare you for assessing students as they work through the unit.
- An Activity Planning Chart shows types of activity, time required, materials, and line masters you will need.
- Materials and Equipment charts list the materials needed for each activity in sequence and also provide a master list of materials and equipment needed for the complete unit.
- After the activity chart, a list of suggestions is given for speakers and field trips that teachers may include to add interest to the topics covered in the unit.
- A section on student preconceptions provides guidance on students' thinking before they start the unit.

The **Unit Launch**

- helps you assess students' prior knowledge
- shows you how to introduce the unit and the design project
- provides answers to questions in the Communicate section

Each lesson

- shows the time the activity (Work On It) in the lesson takes
- shows the skill focus
- tells you what materials you require
- tells you what learning outcomes/indicators are being addressed and suggest assessment opportunities
- gives scientific background
- helps you get each activity started
- provides information for the Work On It part of the activity, showing whether it is appropriate for groups of students, pairs, or single students
- provides additional background or explanation of experiments as discussed in the Think Again! sections
- provides answers to questions in the Communicate section of the student book

- provides assessment tips for ongoing assessment in **Assessment *for* Learning** charts, which provide suggestions for pointers to indicate that a student understands the concepts covered in the lesson

Notes on the **Design Project** are provided, including notes on the use of a Project Planner line master and a Project Rubric.

End-of-project assessment opportunities are discussed, with suggestions as to how to gather evidence of student achievement and communicate this information to parents.

Answers to **Unit Review: Explain Your Stuff**, a section of short-answer questions, are provided.

Reproducible Line Masters

A set of reproducible line masters is included at the end of each unit. These include:

- Unit Summary
- Key Terms
- Unit Test
- Project Planner
- Project Rubric

Generic line masters are provided at the end of this Program Overview. These include:

- Assessment rubrics
- Learning contexts
- Inquiry skills
- Skills worksheets
- Literacy worksheets

A list of the generic line masters is on page 81–82 of this overview.

Using the *Pearson Science 7* and *Pearson Science 8* Teacher's Resources

Pearson Science 7 and *Pearson Science 8* are each accompanied by a Teacher's Resource that provides all the tools you need to implement a science program. Information to help you plan each unit before you start includes:

- A Unit Indicators Correlation Chart lists indicators within unit outcomes, including references to specific lessons that the indicators are covered in. Opportunities for ongoing assessment are listed to prepare you for assessing students as they work through the unit.
- An Activity Planning Chart shows types of activity, time required, materials, and line masters you will need.
- Materials and Equipment charts list the materials needed for each activity in sequence and also provide a master list of materials and equipment needed for the complete unit.
- After the activity chart, a list of suggestions is given for speakers and field trips that teachers may include to add interest to the topics covered in the unit.
- A section on student preconceptions provides guidance on students' thinking before they start the unit.
- There is pertinent Background Information for each Big Idea of a unit presented in a just-in-time fashion.

Each **Invitation to Explore**:
- has a purpose
- lists any key terms introduced in the section
- lists the skills focus
- has the time the activity takes
- lists if the activity should be done in groups, pairs, or individually
- provides relevant safety notes
- lists the needed materials and equipment
- has helpful activity notes
- has answers to the Focus Your Thoughts exercises

Each **Big Idea:**
- has an introduction

Each lesson within the Big Idea:
- has an Indicator Assessment Chart that shows the specific curriculum indicators covered in each section
- lists the time needed to complete each part of a section
- lists the line masters used in the lesson
- introduces the key terms
- provides background information about the science in the lesson
- provides teaching suggestions, broken down by Explore and Develop, to match the student book
- lists the skills focus

- identifies if it is group, pair, or individual work
- lists the activity focus (open inquiry, guided inquiry, or design)
- lists the equipment and materials needed for the hands-on activities in the lesson
- provides learning strategies for ESL/ELL students
  Note: Terminology in this area is evolving and the term English as an Additional Language (EAL) may be preferred.
- has answers to the Communicate and Check Your Progress exercises

Assessment and Evaluation
- Assessment tips are provided for ongoing assessment in **Assessment *for* Learning** charts, which provide suggestions for pointers to indicate that a student understands the concepts covered in the lesson.

Extensions
Extensions are of three kinds:
- For ESL/ELL
- For Reteaching
- For Enrichment

Project, Unit Summary, and Unit Review
Notes on the project are provided. The Unit Summary lists the Key Concepts of a Big Idea and a number of points related to the Key Concepts. This summary provides a useful checklist for students to use in their review of the content. As well, there are answers to the unit review exercises.

Reproducible Line Masters
At the end of each unit of the Teacher's Guide editable line masters are provided. These include:
- Unit Summary
- Key Terms
- Unit Test
- Project Planner
- Project Rubric

Profiles in the *Pearson Science Program*

Three types of profiles are included in the *Pearson Science Program.* These profiles highlight the achievements of men and women. The aim of these profiles is to promote interesting careers in science and raise awareness about science-related issues in society, as well as to draw upon Indigenous Knowledge through the wisdom of First Nations and Métis Elders and Traditional Knowledge Keepers.

These profiles may be used to engage students, to discuss issues related to science, technology, society and the environment, to pique student interest, and to discuss First Nations and Métis ways of knowing. These profiles may inspire students to go out and conduct interviews of their own.

Ask an Elder or Traditional Knowledge Keeper: In this profile type, Elders impart traditional teaching related to the topic or theme of the unit. For example, in *Pearson Science 6* Unit 3: Principles of Flight, on page 166, Elder Stewart Prosper discusses birds and their significance for ways of living with Mother Earth. In *Pearson Science 7* Unit 1: Interactions within Ecosystems, on page 76, Elder Ivan Morin discusses seasons of change in the northern landscape and the need for consultation with Elders during the process of resource development.

Ask an Expert: This type of profile asks an expert in the field, be it a Hovercraft operator, engineer, etc., to answer a question pertinent to the theme of that unit. An example can be found in *Pearson Science 6* Unit 2: Understanding Electricity, page 108, where Jaclyn Mann, a distribution engineer at SaskPower, explains how electricity is delivered to the home.

Careers and Profiles: "Careers and Profiles" highlight interesting jobs in fields related to the topics of study. In *Pearson Science 6* Unit 1: Diversity of Living Things, on page 25, Dr. Dennis Lehmkuhl shares information about his studies of aquatic insects in Saskatchewan. In *Pearson Science 7* Unit 2: Mixtures and Solutions, on page 153, Nancy Case shares information about the process of solution mining. This type of profile asks an expert in their field, be it home-energy efficiency, or training in the use of heavy-duty mining equipment, to share information or discuss questions pertinent to the theme of that unit. This feature highlights the expertise of men and women in a broad range of careers.

Overview of the *Saskatchewan Science 6–9* Curriculum

> The *Pearson Science* series was originally written for Saskatchewan. As such, many references throughout this document are to the Saskatchewan Science curriculum. Though the references are to a specific curriculum, the instructional design and strategies described in this document work for any science curriculum.
>
> To learn more about the Manitoba Science curriculum, please visit the Manitoba Ministry of Education and Literacy website and search for K-12 curriculum.
>
> http://www.edu.gov.mb.ca/k12/cur/science/scicurr.html
>
> Like Saskatchewan, the Manitoba Science curriculum is based on the Pan-Canadian Protocol for Collaboration on School Curriculum *Common Framework of Science Learning Outcomes K to 12.*

The 2009 Saskatchewan Science curriculum for grades 6–9 replaced the 1998 document as part of the planned provincial curriculum review process. The new provincial program of studies is based on the Pan-Canadian Protocol for Collaboration on School Curriculum *Common Framework of Science Learning Outcomes K to 12* (CMEC, 1997). The new science curriculum is guided by three "broad areas of learning" in the core curriculum which aim (1) to foster lifelong learning, (2) to create a sense of self, community, and place, and (3) to promote engaged citizenship at local and global levels. Moreover, the new program of studies considers these four "cross-curricular competencies": (1) Developing Thinking, (2) Developing Identity and Interdependence, (3) Developing Literacies, and (4) Developing Social Responsibility. The new science curriculum is written to encompass both the "broad areas of learning" and the "cross-curricular competencies" in order to connect them to Saskatchewan's philosophy and goals of education. Indicators that reflect Saskatchewan content; science, technology, society, and environment (STSE); and perspectives of endemic First Nations and Métis voices are some of the ways the new curriculum is tailored for the province. The goal of the renewal process is to update presentation of trends, theories, and ideas in science and technology, and with regard to students, to help foster scientific literacy, and promote an understanding of the relationships among science and technology, society, and the environment.

In the new curriculum, the relationship between these goals and expectations is expressed in the Scientific Literacy Framework diagram (on the next page), which shows the four Foundations of Scientific Literacy, i.e., Knowledge (including Indigenous Knowledge), Skills, Attitudes, and STSE, acquired through the learning contexts of Scientific Inquiry, Technological Problem Solving, STSE Decision Making, and Cultural Perspectives. The overall aim is that acquisition of the Foundations will produce a scientifically literate student.

The new science curriculum uses the language of outcomes and indicators, which align with the first two stages of the Understanding by Design model (Wiggins and McTighe, 2005). **Outcomes** are statements of what students are expected to know and be able to do by the end of a grade in a particular area of study. The outcomes provide direction for assessment and evaluation, and for program, unit, and lesson planning. The outcomes serve as the "desired results" in the first stage of backward design. **Indicators** are representative of what students need to know and/or be able to do in order to achieve an outcome. Indicators represent the breadth and the depth of learning related to a particular outcome. Indicators serve as examples of the type of evidence that teachers would accept to determine if students have achieved the desired learning results. Building on these two stages, teachers then move to stage three and plan learning experiences and instructional activities.

Scientific Literacy Framework

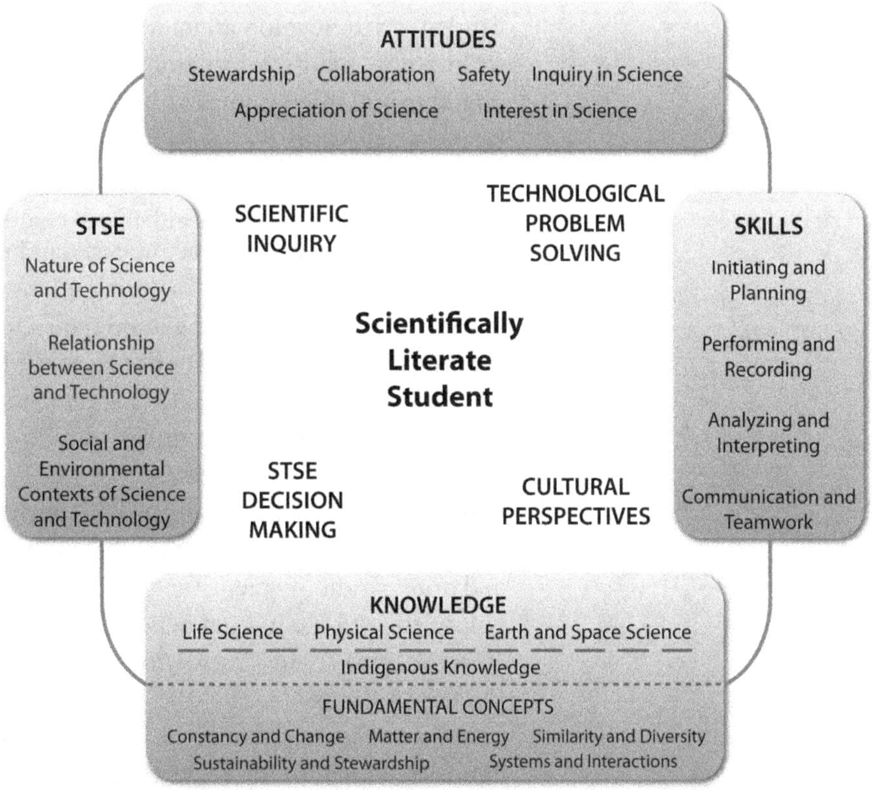

Aims and Goals

The aim of K to 12 science education is to support the development of scientific literacy in all students while considering that scientific literacy today embraces Euro-Canadian and Indigenous heritages. The aim of the Science curriculum is the development of scientific literacy by all students:

Scientific literacy *is an evolving combination of the science-related attitudes, skills, and knowledge students need to develop inquiry, problem-solving, and decision-making abilities to become lifelong learners and to maintain a sense of wonder about the world around them.* (p. 4, Pan-Canadian Protocol for Collaboration on School Curriculum *Common Framework of Science Learning Outcomes K to 12* (CMEC, 1997))

The Ministry of Education has identified four goals for science education. These goals are "*broad statements identifying what students are expected to know and be able to do upon completion of the learning in a particular area of study.*" These goals are written to mirror the foundation statements for scientific literacy identified in the *Common Framework of Science Learning Outcomes K to 12* (CMEC, 1997).

The four goals of K to 12 science are to:

- **Understand the Nature of Science and STSE Interrelationships** – Students will develop an understanding of the nature of science and technology, their interrelationships, and their social and environmental contexts including interrelationships between the natural and constructed world.
- **Construct Scientific Knowledge** – Students will construct an understanding of concepts, principles, laws, and theories in life science, in physical science, in earth and space science, and in Indigenous Knowledge of nature; and then apply these understandings to interpret, integrate, and extend their knowledge.
- **Develop Scientific and Technological Skills** – Students will develop the skills required for scientific and technological inquiry, problem solving, and communicating; for working collaboratively; and for making informed decisions.
- **Develop Attitudes that Support Scientific Habits of Mind** – Students will develop attitudes that support the responsible acquisition and application of scientific, technological, and Indigenous Knowledge to the mutual benefit of self, society, and the environment. (p. 6, *Science 6 (Saskatchewan Curriculum,* 2009))
  [NOTE: All references to the Saskatchewan Science curriculum are to *Science 6*. The front piece (p. i to p. 28) of *Science 6* up to *Science 9* is almost identical in the four grades.]

The main objective of this curriculum, as with many others throughout the world, is to ensure scientific and technological literacy in all students. The *Pearson Science Program* supports the development of scientific and technological literacy in students using the program by providing meaningful contexts, engaging hands-on activities, and student-friendly presentations of basic concepts. *Pearson Science 6* provides activities such as Work On It, Try This at Home, Build on What You Know, and Design Project that help students meet the learning goals. In *Pearson Science 7* and *Pearson Science 8* activities such as Investigator, Technological Problem Solver, and Decision Maker, as well as Experiment on Your Own, Try This at Home, and the unit Project fulfill this role. The Careers and Profiles, Ask an Expert, and Ask an Elder are pieces that help students ground much of the science content within social and environmental contexts. Unit reviews and tests allow options for assessment and evaluation to determine whether goals have been met.

The Foundations of Scientific Literacy

The four foundations of scientific literacy are described in the *Common Framework of Science Learning Outcomes K to 12* (CMEC, 1997). These four foundations are interrelated and comprise the critical pieces of students' scientific literacy.

The Foundations of Scientific Literacy 1: Science, Technology, Society, and the Environment (STSE) Interrelationships

The nature of science and technology and their relationships within the social context in which they are developed are explored. Scientific activity and technological processes may be related and may contribute to each other through innovation. Both are situated within a social context but they are not dependent on each other.

Nature of Science and Technology

The nature of science and technology as it pertains to the revised curriculum are discussed in the first foundation found in the document *Common Framework of Science Learning Outcomes K to 12* (CMEC, 1997).

Within the Saskatchewan curriculum documents (2009), the following statement is made:

Science is a social and cultural activity anchored in a particular intellectual tradition. ... More than most other ways of knowing nature, science excels at predicting what will happen next, based on its descriptions and explanations of natural and technological phenomena. Science-based ideas are continually being tested, modified, and improved as new ideas supersede existing ideas. Technology, like science, is a creative human activity (a way of knowing nature), but is concerned with solving practical problems that arise from human/social needs, particularly the need to adapt to the environment and to fuel a nation's economy. New products and processes are produced by research and development through the processes of inquiry and design. (p. 11, *Science 6 (Saskatchewan Curriculum,* 2009))

The *Pearson Science Program* presents science and technology as distinct but interdependent disciplines, placing emphasis as appropriate in each unit.

Where the focus of science is on the development and verification of knowledge, in technology the focus is on the development of solutions, involving devices and systems that meet a given need within the constraints of the problem. (p. 12, *Science 6 (Saskatchewan Curriculum,* 2009))

The Foundations of Scientific Literacy 2: Scientific Knowledge

The widely accepted disciplines of Life Science, Physical Science, and Earth and Space Science, as reflected in the organization of the units, frame the Scientific Knowledge foundation.

Fundamental Ideas – Linking Scientific Disciplines

Five fundamental ideas have been identified to help students connect their learning from one science discipline to another and to ground the student's knowledge within a larger context. These are strands that run throughout a student's science career from K–12, becoming progressively more elaborate. The ideas are presented in a chart within the Saskatchewan Science curriculum documents, page 15 (2009).

Constancy and Change	The ideas of constancy and change underlie understanding of the natural and constructed world. Through observations, students learn that some characteristics of materials and systems remain constant over time whereas other characteristics change. These changes vary in rate, scale, and pattern, including trends and cycles, and may be quantified using mathematics, particularly measurement.
Matter and Energy	Objects in the physical world are comprised of matter. Students examine materials to understand their properties and structures. The idea of energy provides a conceptual tool that brings together many understandings about natural phenomena, materials, and the process of change. Energy, whether transmitted or transformed, is the driving force of both movement and change.
Similarity and Diversity	The ideas of similarity and diversity provide tools for organizing our experiences with the natural and constructed world. Beginning with informal experiences, students learn to recognize attributes of materials that help to make useful distinctions between one type of material and another, and between one event and another. Over time, students adopt accepted procedures and protocols for describing and classifying objects they encounter, thus enabling them to share ideas with others and to reflect on their own experiences.
Systems and Interactions	An important way to understand and interpret the world is to think about the whole in terms of its parts and alternately about its parts in terms of how they relate to one another and to the whole. A system is an organized group of related objects or components that interact with one another so that the overall effect is much greater than that of the individual parts, even when these are considered together.
Sustainability and Stewardship	Sustainability refers to the ability to meet our present needs without compromising the ability of future generations to meet their needs. Stewardship refers to the personal responsibility to take action in order to participate in the responsible management of natural resources. By developing their understanding of ideas related to sustainability, students are able to take increasing responsibility for making choices that reflect those ideas.

The Foundations of Scientific Literacy 3: Scientific and Technological Skills and Processes

Answering questions, solving problems, and making decisions challenge students to develop the skills of initiating and planning, performing and recording, and analyzing and interpreting within an atmosphere that requires communication and teamwork. The *Pearson Science Program* provides challenges of increasing scope and complexity as students progress through grades 6–8.

Focus on Skills

Teachers are encouraged to promote student achievement by providing their students with opportunities to practise skills. The Saskatchewan Science curriculum encourages teachers to provide experiences where students are challenged. Through laboratory investigations and science challenges, skills such as initiating, planning, performing and recording, analyzing and interpreting, are engaged. Skills of communication and teamwork essential to the development and application of ideas are fostered.

Labs and challenges strengthen a science program and add new levels of interest. However, specific activities are not mandated. For easy reference, the Teacher's Resources for texts in the *Pearson Science Program* identify key skills related to activities and labs. Activities such as Try This at Home, Build on What You Know, and Design Project in *Pearson Science 6* and Experiment on Your Own, Try This at Home, and unit Project in *Pearson Science 7* and *Pearson Science 8* help students hone these skills.

The Foundations of Scientific Literacy 4: Attitudes

Students are encouraged to develop attitudes, values, and ethics for the responsible use of science and technology. Development of scientific literacy will be supported by the following attitudes:

- Appreciation of the contributions and the limitations of science and technology;
- Interest in science at home, at school, and in the community;
- Understanding of the need for evidence and reasoned argument in the development of scientific knowledge;
- Appreciate competence in collaboration with others;
- Awareness of the responsibility for stewardship in society and the environment;
- Concern for safety when engaged in scientific or technological activity.

Focus on Assessment and Evaluation of Student Achievement

As stated in *Science 6 (Saskatchewan Curriculum,* 2009), page 42, *All assessment and evaluation of student achievement must be based on the outcomes in the provincial curriculum.* Three types of assessment contribute to the overall picture of student achievement.

Assessment *for* learning is ongoing through the teaching and learning process and provides information to help students improve their learning. Differentiated instruction may be involved to ensure support of different modes of student learning.

Assessment *as* learning occurs throughout the learning process and involves students' reflection on their own progress in relation to learning associated with curricular outcomes.

Assessment *of* learning occurs at the end of a learning cycle and uses evidence of student achievement of curricular outcomes.

References

Saskatchewan Ministry of Education. *Science 6*. Saskatchewan: Saskatchewan Ministry of Education, 2009. (http://www.education.gov.sk.ca/science-curricula)

Council of Ministers of Education, Canada. *Common Framework of Science Learning Outcomes: Pan-Canadian Protocol for Collaboration on School Curriculum, K–12*. Ontario: Council of Ministers of Education, 1997.

Student Notes

It is highly recommended that students keep notes in a single three-ringed binder. This enables students to draw diagrams, revise rough notes, add material, and submit specific pages to you for evaluation. Students can set up title pages, a table of contents, unit dividers, and a study guide section as an initial homework assignment. The inclusion in the binder of teacher expectations, note-taking skills, and safety rules in handout form is also advisable.

Working with Groups

The *Pearson Science Program* provides a balance of whole-class, small-group, partner, and individual learning opportunities for students to investigate questions, solve problems, take risks, compare results, analyze their findings, and take responsibility for their own learning. Ample opportunity is given for the development of the attitudes described in the fourth foundation of scientific literacy, page 13 of this document.

Whole Class: In *Pearson Science 6,* the **Get Started** section of most lessons in each unit uses large group instruction to introduce new topics and concepts and to model proper techniques for experimenting and recording. Throughout each unit in *Pearson Science 7* and *Pearson Science 8*, there are opportunities to read aloud, dramatize, and clarify understanding with the class as a whole. Both the **Invitation to Explore** introductions and the **Decision Maker** activities encourage dialogue within the class.

Partner and Small Group: Many of the activities found in the *Pearson Science 6* **Work On It, Communicate, Build On What You Know,** and **Project** sections of the lessons and in the *Pearson Science 7* and *Pearson Science 8* **Invitation to Explore**, **Project,** and **Investigator** activities suggest that students work in pairs or small groups. These groupings allow students to develop ideas and solutions to problems that they might not consider if they were working in isolation. In addition, group activities provide students with opportunities to:

- share their ideas readily
- work co-operatively
- learn from each other
- appreciate the capabilities of others
- become more responsible for their own learning
- develop leadership and communication skills

Forming heterogeneous groups based on a range of student abilities will provide opportunities for weaker students to learn from stronger students. This will also help the class develop an appreciation of one another's talents and expertise.

To ensure successful group work and develop students' co-operative work skills, you may like to assign a group role such as Recorder, Materials Manager, Timekeeper, Facilitator, Researcher, and Communicator to each student within the group. Ensure that you rotate roles among students and provide opportunities for students to experience each role.

Some group activities require closer teacher supervision than others because of the hazardous nature of the tools and materials required. One option is to pair each group with a student from a higher grade who is familiar with the tools and materials, who will act as a peer tutor. Another option is to supervise the work of one small group at a time while the rest of the class works on a different activity that requires less supervision.

Individual: The **Communicate, Try This at Home, Unit Review, Explain Your Stuff,** and **How Did You Do?** sections in *Pearson Science 6* and the **Try This at Home, Experiment on Your Own, Project, reSEARCH, Unit Review,** and **Self Assessment** sections in *Pearson Science 7* and *Pearson Science 8* provide opportunities for individual work. The activities in these sections allow students to integrate new knowledge through quiet reflection, to demonstrate their abilities and knowledge, and to incorporate their own interests. The **Try This at Home** sections also provide an opportunity for parents or guardians to become involved with the science program.

Equipment and Materials

Obtaining Materials

You can find many of the materials you need for a successful science program at school (paper clips, modelling clay, cardboard, and the like) and at home (balloons, nails, mirror, flour, and the like). Before you begin a new unit, check the list of required materials for the activities and send a letter home with students requesting donations of the required materials.

You may be able to obtain more specialized science equipment from your local secondary school. Contact the head of the science department and discuss your program needs and equipment requirements. There may also be potential for sharing of science kits among schools within your division.

Local businesses can also be useful sources of materials. Often, they are happy to provide the neighbourhood school with classroom materials. An electrician might be able to provide scrap wire; a building contractor, pieces of insulation and wood, and the local hardware, leftover or returned hardware items. School science supply companies are another source of materials. They sell more specialized items such as alligator clips, plastic tubing, and syringes.

Storing Materials

Open shelves and plastic bins are invaluable for organizing required materials and equipment. Label the shelves and bins to keep things orderly and encourage students to put objects back in their proper places.

There are two approaches to organizing classroom materials and equipment. The first promotes student independence and responsibility. All materials and equipment, with the exception of chemicals and other hazardous products, are stored on labelled shelves and in bins accessible to students. When the class works on an activity, each group or pair of students is responsible for collecting the materials they need and for returning the materials to their appropriate places when they are finished. You will probably find that this approach requires a few extra minutes of class time for students to collect and return the materials.

The second approach saves on class time but requires more teacher preparation. All materials and equipment necessary for an activity or experiment are placed in labelled bins and distributed to groups or pairs of students and then collected at the end of the period. A checklist of the bin items is included with each bin and students are responsible for checking that all items are returned to the bins.

Check the safety guidelines for safe storage of chemicals used in the *Pearson Science Program* on page 73 of this document.

Technology Materials

Much of the equipment necessary for the technology activities in the *Pearson Science Program* is common and readily available. You may like to pool your resources with those of other teachers and assemble design and technology kits to share among the classes on a sign-out basis. Make the kits out of large plastic bins, with lids, in which equipment can be stored. In each kit, include an equipment checklist. You can borrow many of the tools required for the kits, such as hammers, drills, and saws, from home or the local high school. Assign student monitors to check the kits to keep them up to date and complete.

If equipment is limited, schedule time for small groups to use the kits so that all students have an opportunity to use the equipment. Encourage students to reuse and recycle the consumable materials, such as wood and construction paper. When students are working with technology tools, it is wise to increase the amount of supervision in your classroom. You may like to have parent volunteers supervise small groups of students.

Use of Computer Technology

You may wish to use in-class computers or schedule time in the school computer lab to access computer technology to support teaching and learning. Recommended examples of the use of computer technology are:

- For data collection and analysis: using data loggers to collect and analyze data, and database and spreadsheet software to facilitate analysis and display of data.
- For visualization and imaging: using simulation and modelling software may increase student access to some concepts; collecting digital images and video recordings may add to data.
- For communication and collaboration: valid opportunities for networking and participating in projects are available on the Internet. **You should be aware of the need for supervision and provision of adequate safeguards against exploitation of students through Internet access.**

Constructivism in the Science Classroom

The Construction of Knowledge

Halfway through a first period Monday morning science class, a teacher and her class were surprised when a bat suddenly began to fly around their classroom. The bat, which had somehow managed to get into the school over the weekend, had been roosting quietly on the ceiling when it was startled by student voices. Science that day became a lesson in how well bats can fly in a classroom as the teacher struggled to capture the bat. Over the next few days, the teacher was able to draw on the flood of questions about bats to continue with the unit on sound, illustrating points by using the example of how bats navigate during flight by echolocation.

Science teachers often capitalize on such experiences to help students understand science concepts. Newspaper articles, popular television shows, features in science magazines, and local events routinely become part of science lessons as teachers build on existing student interests to make science a motivating and relevant subject.

Less common are attempts by teachers to discover the prior experiences and beliefs students bring to science classrooms and how these experiences relate to the students' ability to learn science concepts. Over the past four decades, research in science education has clearly shown that every student has a unique mind that is constantly engaged in the construction of understanding as he or she makes sense of new ideas within the framework of pre-existing beliefs and ideas. How students make sense of the new ideas presented in science classes clearly depends on the students' life experiences and a myriad of complex factors such as the students' family situation, religious beliefs, or gender. These factors result in a unique and dynamic framework of thinking for each student that affects how the student comes to understand scientific concepts.

What is Constructivism?

The belief that students actively construct new knowledge and understanding based on their pre-existing patterns of thinking and beliefs is called *constructivism* (or *constructivist learning theory*). Most science teachers incorporate some aspects of constructivist learning theory in their practice, especially when they link science concepts to students' prior learning when introducing a new idea. For example, a teacher beginning a unit on substances and mixtures might remind students of times they may have created mixtures when following a recipe or of mixtures they may see in everyday life, such as a granola bar or even a pizza. Even though each student has a unique frame of understanding, most science teachers assume that students have enough common experiences to provide the conceptual links for science concepts to be learned accurately and well.

Research suggests, however, that teachers should question this assumption. In some cases, students' individual prior understandings or preconceptions complement what is taught in science classrooms, leading to a deeper understanding of the science topic. It is much more common, however, that students' existing ideas and beliefs vary considerably and that these prior understandings compete with what they are taught. The result is often a confusing blend of ideas or the outright refusal by students to believe the ideas presented in their science classes! This was demonstrated by a group of pre-service science teachers who, prior to an activity, argued that the heavier an object, the faster it will fall. Every one of these university students had successfully completed senior courses in secondary school physics, claiming to have learned well the principles and calculations for objects in free fall. Only when they dropped similar balls of very different densities at the same time did these university students finally come to change their beliefs, often with gasps of total amazement.

Research into how students construct beliefs and ideas reveals that, once in place, a preconception is very resilient. Studies on the development of students' concepts have discovered that usual practices of science education can make preconceptions worse. A good example is a study that found grade 3 children understand that when water evaporates, the water turns into "tiny particles" which exist in the air. Students in junior high school, however, were more likely to explain that through evaporation the water turns into oxygen and hydrogen gas! Researchers discovered that over time, students accommodated their prior beliefs about evaporation by blending new scientific terminology with their prior knowledge, creating a misconception. In other words, students learned very well how to make "scientific noises," which then led to the development of the misconception. Most disturbing of all is that decades of research on how students learn science concepts reveals that students hold misconceptions about practically every science topic in the school curriculum and that these views interfere with the ability of students to learn science.

Being a Constructivist Teacher

Constructivist learning theory uses such research to develop teaching practices in science education that ensure students learn science concepts accurately. This approach not only exposes and deals with students' preconceptions but also provides a pedagogy that more accurately reflects how scientists work while opening the world of science to students' experiences and backgrounds. In this way, constructivism in science education helps students acquire the scientific literacy needed to be informed, active citizens in today's changing world through the development of a critical understanding of the world of science and by ensuring students learn science concepts well.

Since most people learn best through experience, constructivism argues that it is important for teachers to adapt teaching approaches to match how students learn by adopting a highly experiential, hands-on teaching methodology. Most successful science teachers incorporate hands-on activities when teaching students science concepts. Typically, these activities, or "labs," follow teacher-led introductions to the science topic. Constructivist learning theory argues that this approach is backwards to how most people learn, suggesting that teachers should begin their science classes with concrete, hands-on experiences and from these experiences begin to develop science concepts with students actively involved in the development process. For example, teachers might begin a physics lesson on free fall by challenging students to find a rule about how objects fall. From student experiences of dropping objects, the science class can then lead to a discussion that will reveal that the mass of an object does not affect the rate of fall. In this way, the lesson moves from a concrete experience to the abstract concept, not the reverse.

There are many reasons to begin teaching a science concept with experiences that lead to concept development.

- First, preliminary explorations through experience will help the teacher gauge the extent to which students already understand the science concept. Suppose students have already studied a topic in considerable depth as part of their elementary school education. Without first determining the extent to which students know a topic, teachers might miss a valuable opportunity to develop a topic beyond the boundaries of the mandated curriculum. Or perhaps a teacher might assume students learned a particular topic in elementary school when students may vary considerably in background.
- Second, teachers who explore student understanding through hands-on activities are provided with a valuable opportunity to uncover misconceptions. Once these misconceptions have been identified, teachers can modify their lesson plans to include activities that directly challenge students' prior beliefs.
- Third, beginning science education with hands-on experiences helps develop students into a community of scientists. Science thus becomes an invitation to exploration where knowledge co-emerges through interactions among students, the teacher, the student book, and other resources. In this way, the authority for knowledge development shifts from the teacher to a group process that more accurately reflects how scientists work.
- Finally, the discussion that follows the experience allows students to contribute insights that may be overlooked in a lesson that begins with an abstract idea. For example, a class discussion of what students observed through their examination of living things could provide an opportunity to enrich science education as students share viewpoints from their various cultural backgrounds on the classification of living things.

"Hands On, Minds On"

Constructivism is not discovery learning. Students seldom "discover" scientific concepts independently through hands-on investigation; rather, new concepts must be presented when students are in a receptive state. Often, this is when they have been confronted with the inadequacy of their views in explaining an observation they have made in an activity. The classroom discussions with both teacher and fellow students should guide a pupil in assimilating hands-on experiences and integrating them into new concepts. This method is sometimes called "hands on, minds on," to emphasize the importance of restructuring students' preconceptions through both discussion and hands-on investigation.

Most adults retain at least some preconceptions about scientific concepts. Be aware that such ideas can restrict further understanding of science both for the teacher and for the student, and try to identify and challenge your own misconceptions. Finally, note that computer-based simulations are becoming more available. These will help to challenge student preconceptions by providing a visual approach to concepts that previously could only be presented theoretically. For example, if students see a simulation of the movement of particles of a substance as states change and can alter variables such as temperature, they may be better able to grasp the Particle Theory. Take full advantage of these aids as they become available for your classroom.

Incorporating Language and Literacy into a Science Program

Why Integrate Language and Literacy Instruction?

Many students need some support or guidance from teachers in order to understand the language of science lessons, comprehend grade-level science texts, and write about science topics. The language of science is a new language for many students because it is not encountered in most daily activities. Also, some students may be at various stages of learning English as a second language (ESL)—a process that takes a minimum of five years from their first exposure to an English-language school environment. (Again, note that in many jurisdictions, English as an Additional Language (EAL) is the terminology preferred to ESL.)

Therefore, it is important to use the content of science to:

- emphasize the importance of language use from a holistic perspective
- encourage small-group discussion, emphasizing listening and speaking skills
- review pragmatic and textual cues in reading and writing
- develop students' reading skills, emphasizing viewing of information and representing concepts
- expand students' active vocabulary
- highlight important language patterns
- support or "scaffold" students' writing

How to Encourage Group Discussion

All students need many opportunities to explore ideas and clarify information through group discussion. Group work is especially beneficial for ESL students, who need many opportunities to speak English, but may feel shy or anxious about doing so in front of the whole class. However, effective group work may not happen unless you use specific strategies, such as the following, to ensure that all students are actively involved:

- **Generate ideas through group brainstorming.** Group brainstorming gives all students an opportunity to take risks in a way that they may be reluctant to do in front of the class. It is useful as an introductory activity or a pre-reading strategy to activate prior knowledge, and to generate questions.
- **Help students review, internalize, or apply new concepts and information through group rehearsal.** For example, after a classroom presentation of new material, pose a review or extension question to the whole class. Instead of asking for volunteers to answer the question, instruct students to discuss the question in their groups, and inform the class that you will select, at random, an individual from a group to answer the question.

- **Organize "jigsaw" activities and projects** to encourage students to take responsibility for specific tasks and to value each other's contributions. In a "jigsaw" activity, each student in the group becomes the group "expert" on a different topic and then shares the information with the rest of the group.
- **Teach group skills and language.** Group work provides an ideal opportunity for helping all students develop a repertoire of collaborative skills such as taking turns, staying on task, seeking consensus, and managing controversy and disagreement. Many of these skills involve the use of specific language expressions, some of which need to be explicitly taught, especially when there are second-language learners in the class. Provide opportunities for students to talk about the language they can use to improve group process. For example, say something like, "I noticed that not everybody was taking turns in the conversation, and some people were getting more than their fair share of turns to talk. I wonder what we can say when we want to take a turn, or offer a turn to someone who may be rather shy? What can we say if someone is speaking too much? How can we help the students who are just learning English?"

How to Review Pragmatic and Textual Cues in Reading and Writing

Students may need help to explore the different types of text within their textbook and to understand the organization of each type. While the situation and audience (students of a specific grade) remain the same, different features in the text have different purposes in the presentation of science content. You may wish to point out the conventions followed. For example, in *Pearson Science 6* students could compare the conventions followed in those Work On It sections in which there is a numbered step-by-step procedure with the descriptive or narrative aspects of the Ask an Expert, Ask an Elder, or Careers and Profiles pieces. In supporting and "scaffolding" students' writing in Grade 6 you may wish to highlight the different purposes of say, a report on an experiment such as that in Unit 2, pages 131–133, and a descriptive answer such as that to Try This at Home, "A Visit in Space," Unit 4, page 267.

Similar examples exist in *Pearson Science 7* and *Pearson Science 8*. You could have students compare the conventions followed in Investigators, in which there is a numbered step-by-step procedure, with the descriptive or narrative aspects of the Decision Makers or Careers and Profiles pieces. In supporting and "scaffolding" students' writing you may wish to highlight the different purposes of say, a report on an experiment, and a descriptive or persuasive answer.

How to Develop Students' Reading Skills

To help your students get the most out of the text, you may wish to use a three-stage process known as guided reading (sometimes also called directed reading).

In guided reading, the teacher intervenes between students and text, providing guidance and direction so students can gain information from texts that are beyond their independent reading level, and develop a repertoire of strategic reading skills. With frequent practice, students internalize strategies that help them to become more independent readers of difficult material. Many students benefit from this kind of support throughout elementary school and beyond.

The three stages in the guided, or directed, reading process are outlined below.

Before Reading

Use some of the following activities to prepare the students for the material they are going to read.

- **Help students link new information to prior learning.** For example, some students may have seen or know interesting things about the science topic the class is about to study. Encourage students to bring to class visual material and objects related to the theme to make a classroom collection. Display items can be labelled in the students' own languages, as well as in English. You may wish to have parents or caregivers help with this. Involving and respecting input from the student's home environment will assist with developing the holistic perspective on language use.
- **Have students page through their books to get an initial sense of the structures of the text**. Direct their attention to helpful features such as the table of contents and the headings that indicate specific elements of each unit. **Work On It** and **Think Again!**, in *Pearson Science 6*, and numbered subsections of each Big Idea in *Pearson Science 7* and *Pearson Science 8* are good features to point out. Other such features are the materials and equipment list, the numbered steps in a procedure, and various kinds of visual material.
- **Set the stage and prepare students conceptually** for the material they are going to read. Use the **Launch** activities or **Invitation to Explore** suggested for each unit, which are intended to set the stage.
- **Read aloud the introductory material** for the unit and have students follow along in their books.
- **Pre-teach key words** that will greatly enhance students' comprehension of the text.
- **Provide a graphic organizer** based on the text to show students how the information is organized.

During Reading

Provide guidance and commentary on specific sections of the text in order to develop strategic reading skills such as skimming to get a general idea, returning to read specific sections in more detail, or finding word meanings by using context or word analysis skills. Use the following strategies:

- **"Chunk" the text** into manageable sections. In the student book, the headings make it easy for students to identify specific chunks of text they should focus on.
- **Provide a pre-reading question** related to the main idea of each "chunk" of text and write it on the board.
- **Instruct students to read silently,** skimming for the main idea of the passage or section. (Developing readers and students who are in the first one or two years of learning English as a second language may finger-point, use a ruler to guide their eyes across the page, or subvocalize. As they become more confident and more proficient at extracting meaning from the text, these behaviours will disappear.) Encourage students to keep on reading when they encounter words they don't know.
- **Read difficult sections aloud** and have students follow along in the text, so they hear how words are pronounced and students who are learning English get a feel for phrasing and intonation. It is especially important to read aloud sections that may have difficult new words. Reading aloud also provides an opportunity to demonstrate how to deal with new words. For example, you may like to use a "think-aloud" approach to show how context and background knowledge can help the reader infer the meaning of new words.
- **Stop after each section** to check that students have identified the main idea or can answer the pre-reading question. You can use group rehearsal to make these questions more effective. Answer students' questions before moving on to the next section of text.

What about students reading aloud?
Reading aloud unfamiliar material is not normal reading behaviour, and may actually interfere with comprehension. It is quite common for some students to perform well in oral reading but then be unable to answer comprehension questions on the text. It is equally common for students to stumble and falter through a reading passage that they are able to comprehend when they read it silently.

Reading aloud unfamiliar material is especially difficult for ESL students. These students are often concentrating more on pronunciation than on comprehension, and may be so anxious about performance that they get little or no meaning from what they are reading aloud.

Having students read aloud is a useful activity when students are familiar with the material and when the focus is not on comprehension but on some other aspect of performance, such as locating and identifying specific information in a text, producing the stress and intonation patterns of English, or giving a dramatic interpretation.

After Reading

This stage helps students review what they have read and encourages them to go back to check details that they might have missed the first time. You may also like to direct their attention to specific words or language patterns. Depending on the needs of your students, you may choose to do only one or two of the following activities, or to use some of your language arts time for language development activities related to the science unit.

- **Discuss** what students now know about the topic.
- **Refer the students to the text** to find specific details that exemplify, support, or clarify the main idea, concept, or principle. Encourage students to read aloud the exact word(s) or sentence(s) that answer a specific question posed by the text or by you. Review the variety of ways that concepts are represented, e.g., in diagrams, flow charts, or within photographs.
- **Focus on specific words** in the unit. These may be technical words that are explained in the text, or general words that may have an unfamiliar meaning in this context. You can also use words from the unit to reinforce spelling patterns.
- Use words from the text to develop the students' skills in **word analysis.**
- Provide **review activities** such as completing a graphic organizer or a cloze passage based on the lesson or activity.

How to Expand Students' Active Vocabulary

- You may wish to use vocabulary from the text to increase your students' knowledge of science words, and to learn some word roots and affixes that will enhance their language awareness and vocabulary skills in all areas of the curriculum.
- Introduce your students to the **Anglo-Saxon and Latin roots of English.** Explain that everyday words such as *man, woman, school, house, big, old, eat, sleep,* and *rock* come from the original English language, Anglo-Saxon, the language of the Angles and Saxons who settled in Britain long ago. The name England means "Land of the Angles" (Angle-Land). Anglo-Saxon words usually have only one or two syllables, and English-speaking children learn many of these words before they even come to school. Starting about grade 4, students also begin learning words that come from Latin, the language of the Romans. Many of the words of science are based on Latin words. For example, the words *science, technology,* and *experiment* all come from Latin. Most Latin-based words are "big words" of two or more syllables. There are similar words in French, Italian, Portuguese, Romanian, and Spanish, because these languages are based on Latin.
- Create **word charts** to show the various forms of a word in a "word family." Expand the students' vocabulary skills by helping them to see relationships among words that they might not otherwise recognize, and supplying additional forms of words that they may not be familiar with.
- Create review activities such as **vocabulary cloze passages** to help students to apply the new vocabulary and review content at the same time. You may choose to focus on new words from the lesson or activity, or the use of the correct form of a word (noun, verb, adjective, etc.) in a "word family."

- Use words from the lesson to teach some important **word roots, prefixes,** and **suffixes.** For example, you can focus on the suffix *–tion* in words such as *formation, location,* and *information* (an abstract noun ending) and ask students to think of other words that have the same suffix. You can also focus on word roots such as *form* (shape) and *loc* (place).
- Provide **pronunciation practice** so students can recognize and use new words orally as well as in print. This is especially important for ESL students. Emphasize the main stress on words of two or more syllables, and point out the stress shift in different forms of a word, such as ***rec**ord, re**cord**; ob**serve**, obser**va**tion;* and the like. Articulate words clearly and invite students to repeat them, in chorus and individually. Each morning, or at the beginning of each lesson, call on individual students to pronounce new words from the day before. If the words are posted on a chart, you can point to a word as each student enters the room and ask the student to say it. In the case of ESL students, you may need to say the word first and have the student repeat it.

Activities to avoid:
Avoid word search activities. These are low-level mechanical tasks that depend only on word recognition, not comprehension, and therefore do not expand students' active vocabulary. Moreover, these activities can be confusing to language learners who may be relatively new to the Latin alphabet or the left-right progression of English script.

Avoid assignments that require students to look up and copy definitions of words and then use the new words in sentences of their own that show the meaning. Students may memorize definitions but still be unable to use the word independently.

How to Highlight Important Language Patterns

Some of the language patterns that are commonly used in science lessons and texts may be unfamiliar to some students, especially those who are learning English as a second language. You may like to use the content of the science lesson to provide mini-lessons on some of the sentence patterns of English to individual students or groups of students:

- Highlight **transition words** that indicate specific kinds of thinking. For example, you can begin a chart of words and phrases that indicate comparison and contrast: *similar to, different from.* This chart can be added to in subsequent lessons.
- Draw attention to **passive verbs,** which are commonly used in science to describe processes and to write lab reports, but are relatively uncommon in day-to-day language use.
- Help students to "unpack" **condensed expressions** such as:
  monuments built of rock = *monuments* **that have been** *built of rock*
  those collected by your classmates = *those* **that have been** *collected by your classmates*

groups based on the characteristics = *groups* **that are** *based on the characteristics*

- Use the content of the chapter to devise simple cloze sentences for ESL students, focussing on particular **grammatical forms** such as plurals, past tense, possessives, and subject-verb agreement.

Review and reinforcement

It takes at least five years for ESL students to become proficient in English sentence structure. Therefore, these patterns will need constant review and reinforcement over a period of several years.

How to Support or "Scaffold" Students' Writing

While some of your students may be able to write quite independently, others—especially students who are learning English as a second language—will need plenty of support or "scaffolding" to complete their written assignments. You may wish to provide:

- **models of various forms of writing,** with an emphasis on the audience and purpose for writing. Examples include
  - *Report*: A report uses subheadings to organize well-chosen facts from reliable sources on a specific topic. The report typically makes a number of recommendations based on directions indicated through the research.
  - *Analysis*: Similar to a report, an analysis involves researching background information on several situations, possibilities, or options and then summarizing the pertinent details in a form, such as a chart. The information is then analyzed, the options evaluated, and a final decision reached.
  - *Chronological Organization or Sequential Pattern*: Writers use chronological or sequential organization when they want to explain in historical sequence or in a series of steps what happened or how to do something. This pattern can be recognized easily by the presence of signal words such as *first*, *second*, *then*, *next*, *after*, and *finally* or by the inclusion of particular dates.
  - *Problem–Solution or Cause-and-Effect Pattern*: Writers use a problem–solution or cause-and-effect pattern when they want to explain or report why something is happening. This pattern can be identified by the presence of signal words such as *since*, *when*, *if*, *because of*, *in order to*, and *as a result*.
  - *Graphic Organizers*: Graphic organizers can be used to organize information visually. Students should be familiar with Venn diagrams, tree diagrams, concept maps, etc.
  - *Narrative Lab Report*: The narrative lab report lets the student tell the story of an investigation by writing an essay that answers four questions: What were we looking for? How did we look for it? What did we find? and What does this mean?

- Students should also be familiar with bulleted lists (for equipment and materials lists), scientific and technical drawings with labels, tables, and graphs. These elements of scientific writing are covered in the Toolkits in the student textbooks.
- **writing prompts** to get students started. For example, to get students started in answering Communicate questions, provide prompts like:
  I found the _____ test the most interesting because...
  The thing that surprised me most about our results was...
- **cloze passages** to help students use new words or specific sentence patterns

Literacy—The Reading and Writing Connection

Reading and writing are intricately connected. When readers and writers share the same understanding of how a text is constructed, they are able to communicate easily. The many decisions a writer makes in terms of audience, topic, and format will contribute to how well readers are able to understand the text. Readers who understand the writer's decision-making process and who can recognize the organizational patterns used are able to focus their attention more on the meaning of what they are reading.

Connecting Reading and Writing in the *Pearson Science Program*

Students need guidance when writing in order to assist them in thinking critically about and communicating ideas, opinions, and problems and solutions in science. Strategies and their purposes must be explicitly taught through teacher modelling and scaffolding until students can independently choose and use them while writing. See the line master table of contents for generic line masters that support these literacy strategies. As students become more familiar with each of these frameworks, they can also use them as note-taking tools or graphic organizers when they are reading.

Differentiated Instruction
by Karen Hume

What Is Differentiated Instruction?

There is no need to differentiate all day, every day. (Karen Hume, author)

Differentiated instruction is instruction that has a significant, positive impact on student achievement and involves the teacher making small alterations to successful, effective practices in order to respond to an individual's readiness, interests, or learning preferences.

Differentiation is an organizing framework for everything that happens in teaching and learning. The first half of the definition refers to instruction that is, first of all, effective—instruction that has a significant, positive impact on student achievement. The second half of the definition refers to instruction that is responsive—the making of small alterations to successful, effective practices in order to respond to an individual's readiness, interests, or learning preferences.

Let's look at each part of the definition in turn. To ensure effective instruction, teachers plan using the model of backward design developed by Grant Wiggins and Jay McTighe. This model has three steps:

1. Identify the learning intentions of the unit in some detail and frame those intentions in the form of big ideas and essential questions so that students are involved in inquiry.
2. Determine the assessments for, as, and of learning that will be used at all stages of the learning to determine what students know, understand, and are able to do. Assessments for and as learning are used to determine next steps in instruction. Assessments of learning evaluate student understanding and skill.
3. Plan activities that are aligned to the learning intentions and assessments. Activities are based on powerful instructional strategies, such as the list generated by Robert Marzano's review of the last 35 years of educational research, and may be differentiated as needed or desired. Strategies are taught and assessed in the context of a strong learning community, one in which students are aware of their own strengths and needs, and supportive of the strengths and needs of others.

Differentiation applies to students in all classes and to students with special needs, English as an additional language learners, and gifted students. Learning happens only when teachers "start where they are" (Hume, 2008), meaning that teachers build on students' prior knowledge and link to their readiness, interests, or learning preferences.

To ensure responsive instruction, teachers are aware of the readiness, interests, and learning preferences of the learner and offer the appropriate degree of challenge to significantly increase both student engagement and academic success.

1. Readiness

What Is It?

Students are at different points of readiness for learning different concepts based on their background knowledge of that concept. Think of readiness as being on a continuum with three points:

Emerging ⟷ On Track ⟷ Advanced

Why Is It Important?

Readiness is a more positive and useful term than ability. All learners are at different points of readiness for different concepts, depending on their background knowledge; no learner is a struggling student all of the time.

How Do Teachers Determine a Student's Readiness?

Readiness can be determined only through assessments for learning. Teachers should ensure that pre-assessments and formative assessments are targeted to address exactly what they need to know about student understanding of key concepts. If teachers use the unit openers to make students aware of the skills they will use and the concepts they will learn over the course of the unit, they can help the students see their growth in understanding from "emerging" to "on track" or "advanced."

How to Support Different Points of Readiness

- Create tiered assignments. Tiered assignments provide different levels of the same activity to meet the differing stages of readiness for the concept being taught. The easiest way to create a tiered assignment is to either begin with or create an activity for "on track" students and then modify it by varying in either direction according to one or more of the considerations in the following chart:

	Emerging Readiness	**On Track**	**Advanced Readiness**
Concepts	Concrete	Mostly concrete, with some abstraction	Abstract
Procedure	Minimal number of steps to complete the assignment	Can require more steps to complete the assignment	Can be more open-ended, leaving decisions about how the assignment is completed to the student
Reading Level	Appropriate to participants; may be below grade level	At grade level	Above grade level
Teacher Support	Teacher may model or partially complete the activity to provide examples.	Teacher provides some verbal or written support.	Teacher provides support as needed.

- Use short-term flexible learning groups. Teachers may physically group students or just mentally group students according to the assignment, choosing homogeneous groupings based on readiness or heterogeneous groupings where students at different readiness points work together.

2. Interest

Why Is It Important?

Engagement and expertise go hand in hand with students' areas of interest. Since their interests influence students' background knowledge, and since learning happens only when building on prior understanding, knowing students' areas of interest helps teachers to make relevant connections to support those who are at an emerging point of readiness for a key concept.

How Do Teachers Determine Students' Interests?

Casual conversations are the fastest and easiest way to determine students' interests.

How to Support Students' Interests

- Use knowledge of students' interests to provide relevant connections when a student is struggling with a key concept.
- Provide students with exit cards at the end of class. An exit card is an index card where students respond to a prompt. For example, the teacher might ask students to talk or write about the similarities and differences between the day's lesson and an area of interest.

3. Learning Preferences

What Are They?

There are two categories of learning preferences that are often considered in the differentiated classroom:

- Learning styles refer to the ways an individual acquires and processes information. The most commonly referenced learning styles are represented by the acronym VAK — visual, auditory, and kinesthetic.
- Intelligence preferences refer to the ways in which an individual naturally tends to work when confronted with a difficult problem or when creating something new. Howard Gardner's multiple intelligences are one grouping of intelligence preferences; Robert Sternberg's triarchic intelligences are another.

Why Are They Important?

Because learning preferences refer to the natural ways in which we learn, students have an easier time learning new concepts when they are allowed to work according to their preferences.

How Do Teachers Determine a Student's Learning Preferences?

Use inventories (Hume, 2008), or provide learning stations that allow students to learn or practise a concept in a variety of forms and observe their responses.

How to Support Student Learning Preferences

- Teach the whole class a single concept in a variety of forms. Fortunately, science teachers have a wonderful advantage in being able to offer plenty of opportunities for kinesthetic activity through science experiments.
- Allow students to sometimes choose their preferred way of working. A good rule of thumb is to allow students to work according to their strengths when a concept is tough, and to push students to work in areas that aren't strengths when a concept is easy.

Differentiation is based on teachers knowing their learners, but they do not need to know everything about each of the many students they teach. There is also no need to differentiate all day, every day. Rather, teachers can use their understanding of students' readiness, interests, or learning preferences and their knowledge of the curriculum to "tweak" currently successful practices around key concepts so they will reach a few more learners.

For further information and lots of practical suggestions about how to differentiate instruction, refer to:

Hume, Karen. *Start Where They Are: Differentiating for Success with the Young Adolescent*. Toronto: Pearson Canada, 2008. (with 88 modifiable line masters)

Ontario Ministry of Education. Differentiated Instruction Educator's Package. Toronto: Student Success Training, Implementation and Evaluation Branch, 2007.

References

Gardner, Howard (2006) *Multiple Intelligences: New Horizons.* New York: Basic Books.

Marzano, Robert (2003) *What Works in Schools: Translating Research into Action.* Virginia: ASCD.

Sternberg, Robert (1996) *Successful Intelligence.* New York: Simon & Schuster.

2 Assessment and Evaluation

Planning for Assessment

Clear Targets and Criteria for Success

The aim of K–12 science education is to support development of scientific literacy in all students while considering that scientific literacy today embraces Euro-Canadian and Indigenous heritages. Specific goals within this aim identify what students are expected to know and be able to do upon completion of study in a particular area.

The goals for students in K–12 science are to:

- understand the nature of science and STSE interrelationships
- construct scientific knowledge
- develop scientific and technological skills
- develop attitudes that support scientific habits of mind

Student assessment is one of the most important tasks in the teaching-learning process and when considering assessment and evaluation, you must think in terms of the goals for students. Assessment advocate Rick Stiggins asserts that, "Students can hit any target they can see that holds still for them." Students need to begin their learning journey with the end in mind. In *Pearson Science* the Big Ideas of science that are to be covered are listed at the beginning of each unit. You may want to identify the outcomes for each strand from the Saskatchewan Science curriculum documents (2009) to let students know what they are expected to know and be able to do by the end of the grade. Introducing the unit project at the beginning of a unit further supports "beginning with the end in mind" by providing students with a greater purpose for working through the unit.

Research indicates that when students see themselves in the curriculum, they experience greater success. The *Pearson Science Program* relates the text to students' lives by use of familiar scenes and stories.

Effective teachers incorporate assessment strategies into all aspects of their teaching; students who know how the assessment process works and who feel their input is valued usually have a greater sense of ownership in their learning. Sharing assessment criteria with students helps them identify what constitutes a range of performances and is a vital step in the assessment process. Rubrics or scoring guides should also be given to students prior to the assessment. Involving students in the development of rubrics is extremely desirable, and the inclusion of editable rubrics should further help to support this.

Examining anchor text of student work helps students better understand criteria, and providing them with examples that demonstrate a range of performances (e.g., Levels 1, 2, 3, 4) rather than a single example is indeed beneficial. This not only promotes clarity on what a particular performance looks like, but also helps students to differentiate between the levels of performance, an important Assessment *as* Learning skill. Student examples shared with students should not have student names on them.

Eight rubrics have been developed specifically to support the key features of the Saskatchewan Science curriculum. These include rubrics for the four Learning Contexts (Scientific Inquiry, Technological Problem Solving, Cultural Perspectives, and STSE Decision Making), which represent different methods of engaging students' inquiry in science. Each rubric addresses aspects of the four Foundations of Scientific Literacy (Knowledge, Skills, STSE, and Attitudes). Teachers may use these rubrics to assess student learning of the outcomes in a particular unit, or part of a unit.

Four other rubrics assess the four Skills of Scientific Literacy (Initiating and Planning, Performing and Recording, Analyzing and Interpreting, and Communication and Teamwork). These rubrics are designed to be used independently of the Learning Context rubrics. Teachers may choose to use one or more of these rubrics at various times throughout the year. It is not necessary for teachers to obtain evidence of student abilities related to these skills for every investigation.

Teachers can use these rubrics as is, or modify them to meet their needs.

Balanced Assessment

Incorporating different types of assessment and evaluation strategies throughout a unit or topic provides each student with the opportunity to be assessed or evaluated as part of an ongoing process. Assessment in these cases is not an end in itself. In order to be responsive to student differences and to arrive at valid inferences about student achievement, it is imperative that you triangulate data using a variety of assessment strategies. Students must be provided with multiple opportunities to demonstrate the full extent of their learning, and these assessments should be fair, free from bias, and equitable for all (e.g., arranging accommodations, or using modified learning expectations for English Language Learners).

A balance of products, conversations, and observations should be considered when planning for assessment.

- Products include: slide shows, podcasts, reports, pamphlets, notebooks, tests, quizzes, and graphic organizers
- Conversations include: student conferences, interviews, dialogues, discussions, and oral questioning
- Observations include: scientific investigations, research skills, performance tasks, skill demonstrations, presentations, simulations, and drama activities

Scientific and technological skills and processes provide one of the Foundations of Scientific Literacy. This foundation is discussed on page 16 of *Science 6 (Saskatchewan Curriculum,* 2009). This information provides teachers with a way of looking at what students can do so that they can plan for further development of their students' skills. In general terms, the skills involved are:

- initiating and planning (e.g., formulating questions or hypotheses, making predictions)
- performing and recording (e.g., conducting research, safely conducting inquiries)
- analyzing and interpreting (e.g., evaluating and analyzing data, drawing conclusions)
- communication and teamwork (e.g., using appropriate vocabulary, communicating findings in a variety of ways)

Stages of Assessment

Assessment of *Learning (Summative Assessment)*

Assessment *of* learning is summative in purpose and occurs at the end of a period of learning. Summative assessment is evaluative; it is used to communicate and report to students, parents, guardians, and other stakeholders about students' progress in school.

Although assessment *of* learning occurs at the end of a period of learning, because it gives teachers information about student achievement of curriculum outcomes, it is planned at the outset. Students need to be made aware in advance of which assessments are summative and what criteria will be used to assess their performance. Students should also have had practice with the assessment method(s) being used. Creating summative assessments that meet the needs of your students is easier with modifiable rubrics and unit tests. These are provided in the *Pearson Science Program.*

Summative evaluation applies a judgment to the data collected. These Assessment *of* Learning processes include *design projects, short answer questions,* and *rubrics.* Summative evaluation informs you how well the curriculum goals or outcomes/indicators for the unit have been met, and helps in determining the student's final reporting mark. The focus here has been on achievement of the outcomes by the end of the year. Consideration must be given to the achievement of outcomes that students master later in the year, but which were also assessed earlier in the year when achievement was less complete. Summative evaluation should reflect the latest level of achievement of the outcomes.

Assessment for *Learning* (Pre-Assessment)

In order to determine student readiness and prior knowledge, teachers usually begin the assessment cycle with assessment *for* learning. Units in the *Pearson Science Program* begin with an assessment *for* learning opportunity tied into the unit opener that is designed to activate prior knowledge, determine gaps in learning, uncover alternative understandings, and focus student learning. The teaching notes in this Teacher's Resource provide guidance for teachers unsure how to elicit student understandings of the various topics. The data from the assessment *for* learning may reveal a need to provide some foundational learning prior to moving individual students forward. Content covered in previous grades can be readdressed through Reteaching Strategies found throughout this Teacher's Resource.

Assessment for *and* as *Learning* (Formative Assessment)

Formative assessment includes ways for you to gather, record, and interpret data about the progress and achievement of each child in the class. Moreover, fair and meaningful assessment techniques, in the eyes of all shareholders—students, teachers, and parents—create a climate that will enhance the students' motivation. *Observation records, journals and logs, student self-evaluation, interviews about projects, mini-quizzes,* and *student demonstrations* all comprise formative assessment. Assessment should reflect the scientific and technological skills addressed in a particular activity. Results may be written up using formal lab reports, less-structured narrative lab reports, or a paragraph describing the significance of the findings.

The feedback to students occurs during the course of instruction and provides important and immediate information to them as they work. For you, systematic feedback provides invaluable insight into the need for program modifications. Thus, both assessment *for* learning and assessment *as* learning (*Science 6 (Saskatchewan Curriculum,* 2009), page 42) are formative in nature.

Research indicates that the most effective type of assessment for improving student learning is assessment *for* learning. What distinguishes one type of assessment tool from another depends on how it is used and what is done with the data it generates. For an assessment to be truly *for* learning, it must make a difference when teachers are planning for instruction and assessment of individuals or groups of students. If the assessment data you collect does not inform your instruction, then it is not assessment *for* learning.

Students also have a different role than in the past. Assessment *as* learning supports students learning about themselves as they self-assess, peer-assess, and set goals. Providing students with processing and reflecting time at the end of a class not only supports student understanding of the most recent concepts, but also helps students identify their own strengths and challenges as learners and recognize their growth over time. Developing metacognitive awareness enables students to take advantage of the choices provided within today's classroom.

Descriptive Feedback – An Important Assessment *for* Learning Tool

Feedback to students should be descriptive and specific whether it is written or verbal. "Good job" or "well done" is no more helpful than a checkmark, a numerical mark, or telling a student "this needs improvement" or "you're not quite there yet." If something is well done, then you need to communicate exactly what was well done. For example, "The way you considered the Particle Theory when deciding on materials is a good example of applying your knowledge in an unfamiliar context." Similarly, you need to communicate what specifically needs to be improved upon and offer suggestions to move struggling students forward. For example, "When labelling your diagram, you need to label all forces that are present. Be sure to include both input and output forces."

Descriptive feedback is powerful assessment *for* learning. Research indicates that when teachers provide either marks without comments or marks with comments, students do equally poorly. However, the same research indicates that providing comments only (with no marks) leads to significant increases in student achievement.

There are numerous opportunities for assessment *for* and *as* learning within this program that are supported by features in both the *Pearson Science* student books and this Teacher's Resource.

In the Student Books

- In *Pearson Science 7 & 8* the Communicate sections are strategically placed throughout the development of new content to support understanding. These represent great opportunities to check in with individual students and provide them with descriptive feedback that will guide them toward the learning targets. They can also be used by students in assessing their own learning.
- In *Pearson Science 6* the Communicate sections at the end of each lesson, and in *Pearson Science 7 & 8* the Check Your Progress questions located at the end of a section of new skills and concepts, provide another opportunity to check for understanding prior to moving forward. Correlations between these features and the Outcomes and Indicators of the Saskatchewan Science curriculum documents (2009) are included in the Unit Indicator Correlation Chart at the beginning of each unit in this resource.
- In *Pearson Science 6* the Unit Reviews, and in *Pearson Science 7 & 8* the Check your Progress subsections and the Unit Reviews, are an excellent way for students to assess their own learning as they prepare for assessment *of* learning. **Please note that a wide range of questions have been provided so that teachers can select questions that will be appropriate for the students in their classroom.**

In this Teacher's Resource

Teachers who are generalists may not be aware of what to look or listen for in student performances or what to suggest as next steps. In all Teacher's Resources for the *Pearson Science Program* there are What to Look For boxes that list the key concepts with suggestions to meet the needs of all learners.

While assessment, evaluation, and reporting will always serve the purpose of identifying levels of student performance, their major purpose is to support student growth and improve learning. This core belief must be alive in every classroom.

For further assistance with planning and assessment, refer to:
Hume, Karen. *Evidence to Action: Engaging and Teaching Young Adolescents through Assessment* and *50 Tools and Techniques for Classroom Assessment*—a two-book package with over 100 modifiable line masters and 50 video clips. Toronto: Pearson Canada, 2010.

References

Black, P. and D. Wiliam. Assessment and classroom learning. *Assessment in Education*, 5 (1): 7-74, 1998.

Black, P. and D. Wiliam. *Inside the Black Box: Raising Standards Through Classroom Assessment*. 2001.

Stiggins, Rick, J. A. Arter, J. Chappuis, and S. Chappuis. *Classroom Assessment for Student Learning: Doing It Right-Using It Well*. Portland, OR: Assessment Training Institute, Inc., 2004.

3 Fostering Scientific Knowledge

Overview

Research demonstrates that students have well-formed preconceptions in each of the three strands of science: life science, physical science, and Earth and space science. For example, many students have a restricted view of what the word "animal" means (some think it applies only to four-legged, terrestrial creatures). Some students think that plants get their food from the soil. Some students think that the total mass decreases when sugar dissolves in water. Some students think that rocks and soil have always been as we see them today.

Research also indicates that students are very reluctant to let go of their preconceptions, despite what teachers or textbooks might say, and even despite what they might experience in hands-on investigations. However, if students are encouraged to share their preconceptions before and during investigations, and then reflect on what they believe, they are more open to replacing their preconceptions with scientific understanding in subsequent activities. This is especially true when students discover that their preconceptions don't make sense in light of the new observations they are making.

Pearson Science 6

Pearson Science 6 uses a straightforward, five-step method to help you deal with student preconceptions, as found in Driver and Oldham's book *Studies in Science Education.* The steps of this method are outlined below:

1. **Orientation**—The opening **Launch** in each *Pearson Science 6* unit starts students thinking about the topic.
2. **Elicitation**—The **Communicate** questions at the end of each Launch encourage students to share their ideas about the topic of the unit. Questions embedded throughout the text also facilitate elicitation. You can lead the class in additional activities, such as concept mapping (student book, Toolkit 5), to further elicit student preconceptions and have students make predictions before engaging in the activities of the unit.
3. **Restructuring**—The **Getting Started** sections orient students to the particular concept or topic in that lesson. **Work On It** activities allow students to test their ideas and consider more scientific explanations. This restructuring is more likely to take place when students predict the outcome of an experiment prior to the investigation and discuss the new things they have learned following the investigation. The **Think Again!** sections give the opportunity to review what has been discussed earlier in the lesson, or may add

further interesting facts on the topic. As you discuss with students the new things they have learned from the investigation, and encourage students to discuss these insights with each other, you help this restructuring to occur.

4. **Application**—Students apply their new views or conceptions to other areas or examples. The **Communicate** section provides these opportunities. As well, many lessons have a **Build On What You Know** section that asks students to apply what they are learning throughout the unit in an ongoing way. The **Design Project** at the end of each unit also provides an opportunity for students to apply their ideas to a new problem.
5. **Review of Ideas**—Students solidify their new concepts by reviewing their new ideas in the **Communicate** sections as well as in the **Unit Summary** and **Unit Review** at the end of the unit. The final review is a vital section of the unit, enabling students to cement new ideas they have been exploring.

In the Teacher's Resource for each unit, *Pearson Science 6* discusses student preconceptions about the topics and suggests ways for teachers to address them.

References

R. Driver & V. Oldham, *Studies in Science Education 13* (1986): 105–122

Pearson Science 7 and *Pearson Science 8:* Constructing Science with Students: The EDU Model

Teaching in ways that take into account student thinking and the rich diversity of student backgrounds and experience can seem overwhelming, but a simple model can help organize a constructivist learning theory approach while providing a framework for lesson planning. Several models support constructivist learning. One example is the Biological Sciences Curriculum Study (BSCS) 5E model (Engage, Explore, Explain, Elaborate, and Evaluate). A second model, discussed in detail here, follows three key steps in teaching students science: Explore, Discuss, and Understand. This model is easy to remember since the first letters, EDU, are also the first three letters of the word "education." This application of constructivism is presented in more detail in the section that follows.

In *Pearson Science 7* and *Pearson Science 8* the Explore, Develop, and Communicate icons indicate stages in the process that mirror the constructivist model on the following pages.

Explore

Lessons begin with students examining the ideas about a topic and determining what they already know about that topic. Some constructivist teachers use a pre-quiz or have a discussion to discern the extent of students' prior knowledge and to discover if the students hold any misconceptions about the topic. Once the constructivist teacher is aware of students' prior understanding of the topic, he or she then invites students to engage in hands-on science explorations.

There are three advantages to this approach.

- First, discussions about the science topic in the student book and with the classroom teacher make more sense to students if students first have some experience with aspects of the topic.
- The second benefit is that experience prevents the students from continuing with any preconceptions they may be carrying. For example, students often carry the preconception that animal cells are spherical. This preconception may develop from the stylized "general" cell drawings common to many textbooks. By asking students first what they picture as a cell and then inviting them to actually see many different cells, students are confronted with a challenge to their misconception. The result, according to constructivist learning theory, is "cognitive dissonance" that opens the opportunity for students to change their thinking.
- The third benefit of inviting students to be explorers is the development of a community in which students are engaged in examining and making sense of the natural world, that is, in which they are scientists. These experiences provide rich and valuable opportunities for teachers to discuss with students the nature and process of science.

Discuss

Discussion plays a crucial role in the world of science. Scientists routinely meet informally and formally to discuss their research and discoveries. These meetings provide a chance to correct preconceptions and find new avenues for research; often, new questions emerge which invite further exploration. Science education in the EDU model offers the same parallel as meaning is constructed through discussions following initial explorations. In some cases, the students will have made discoveries that contradict their prior conceptions. Teachers play a key role in this stage by challenging students to explain the discrepancy. Usually, the students realize their prior thinking was incorrect, but sometimes the students will need to engage in further exploration, especially if they remain doubtful. Some students will have new questions arising from their explorations and these may lead to further research or to readings from a textbook or Internet site.

There are many ways to encourage students to share how they make sense of their discoveries. Class conversations, group discussions, assigned readings, casual debates, journal entries, oral reports, or the development of flow charts all require the students to reveal their growing understanding of a science topic. Teachers need to be careful, to allow students to reach conclusions for themselves. The key aspect of this stage of the EDU model involves allowing students to take responsibility for the development of their understanding of a science concept. For example, as part of an Explore activity, teachers might challenge students to compile a list of objects the students believe are alive and others that are not alive. Sharing these lists in the Discuss stage could lead to a discussion on the characteristics of living things, with students encouraged to suggest ways in which these characteristics might be examined in more detail.

The Discuss stage of the EDU model is the ideal time for teachers to help students link their growing understanding of science to ways in which science relates to technology, society, and the environment. With the rapid rise of so many technological innovations, students in the 21st century need to understand that science is not an isolated study but part of the larger working of societies. Once students have the opportunity to discuss the results of their exploration and to examine the meaning created through discovery, teachers will wish to ensure students have effectively learned the science concepts of a lesson. This moves the construction of science knowledge in science education to the next phase in the EDU model.

Understand

Science teachers typically determine student learning through examinations or assignments. Constructivist learning theory accepts the role of such evaluation methods but argues that, since students learn in different ways, teachers should use a wide variety of assessment methods in science education to match student learning styles. The primary purpose of this stage of the EDU model is to reveal the extent and depth of student learning. Student understanding of science concepts will become clear as students are challenged to apply what they have learned about a particular topic.

Activities include creating models, making predictions, designing and performing an experiment, or presenting a dramatization of a scientific process. Throughout these steps, it is important to encourage students to discuss their ideas with each other, so that they can state their preconceptions and check them against other's ideas and against experimental observations. Students then can clarify their thinking by further discussion, and build new ideas by assessing and incorporating the views of their classmates. It is equally important for the teacher to talk through ideas with the class. These discussions, which often occur during hands-on investigations, help students to realize their own misconceptions and allow the teacher to present the accepted view.

Adapted with permission from material provided by Dr. David Blades, University of Victoria

Student Preconceptions

Before you can give someone directions on how to get somewhere, you first have to know where they are.

The mind of the student is not like an empty storage bin, ready to be filled with facts and theories, but already contains well-formed conceptions. Students seldom change these ideas, despite what is presented in science class. They will have built complex cognitive structures around their preconceptions that they use every day to make sense of the world. It is therefore not easy to replace these views with valid scientific conceptions. One very effective approach is to first identify the ideas that students have on a subject, and then to present new information in a way that takes these views into consideration. Rosalind Driver, a researcher who focussed on how children learn science, explains this by analogy to having a visitor who telephones you to ask directions to your house. The most useful starting point is to first ask, "Where are you now?"

Identifying Student Preconceptions

Educational research has identified many preconceptions that students will likely have when beginning intermediate level science. You may also wish to explore your own students' views. Consider the following approaches for your class:

- *Written statements*: Ask students to list five things they know about a lesson topic. Students can then break into small groups to pool and classify their ideas according to their own criteria.
- *Posters*: Ask students to make a poster answering a question central to the ideas to be discussed. Students should discuss the question in a small group first, then create their poster and present it to the class.
- *Card sort*: Provide the class with cards that present examples relevant to the area to be explored. Provide students with an appropriate criterion, then direct them to sort the examples on this basis (e.g., by size, by amount of energy, by strength, by kind).
- *Thought experiment*: Describe an experiment that incorporates the concepts of interest. Challenge students to predict the outcome of the experiment and explain their reasoning. This type of exercise is best performed in small groups. You may also have students perform the experiment to test their ideas against the outcome.
- *Design and make*: Challenge students to solve a problem hands on, using their knowledge of the concepts being explored. Students should work in small groups and discuss and defend their ideas with their group members.
- *Explain:* Ask the students to explain a phenomenon or observation relevant to the concepts to be addressed, such as "Why does sugar dissolve faster when it is stirred?" Have students first write an explanation independently, then discuss it in small groups and present their consensus to the class. Diagrams may also be used.

Developing Students' Skills

The Pan-Canadian Science Project, and provincial curricula that have followed from it, emphasize students' understanding of basic concepts and development of skills. These skills include those necessary for conducting experiments and those necessary for designing and planning experiments, which are referred to as "skills of inquiry and design." Four broad skill areas are outlined in the Saskatchewan Science curriculum documents: Initiating and Planning; Performing and Recording; Analyzing and Interpreting; and Communicating and Teamwork. The *Pearson Science Program* is designed to facilitate acquisition in these skill areas.

To understand basic concepts and develop skills for doing experiments, students benefit from engagement in many hands-on activities that are well planned and organized. The *Pearson Science Program* provides a rich assortment of these activities, which address the specific outcomes and indicators of the Saskatchewan Science curriculum documents. To develop skills of inquiry and design, students must design and plan investigations of their own. The student books provide opportunities for students to ask questions and devise investigations to answer their questions. Thus, students engage in the true processes of inquiry and design.

Inquiry Learning

The Saskatchewan Science curriculum regards inquiry as more than a systematic empirical process. Curriculum documents describe inquiry as *"a philosophical approach to teaching and learning, grounded in constructivist research and methods, which engages students in investigations that lead to disciplinary, interdisciplinary, and transdisciplinary understanding."* (*Science 6 (Saskatchewan Curriculum,* 2009), p. 7) The process builds on students' natural curiosity, providing them with opportunities for investigation, understanding, and reflection. The curriculum further states, *"Inquiry learning is not a step-by-step process, but rather a cyclical process, with various phases of the process being revisited and rethought as a result of students' discoveries, insights, and construction of new knowledge."* (*Science 6 (Saskatchewan Curriculum,* 2009), p. 8)

Students using the *Pearson Science Program* will be able to:

- identify questions that can be answered through inquiry
- design and conduct investigations
- use appropriate tools and techniques to gather data
- analyze and interpret data
- develop explanations, predictions, and models using evidence
- think critically and make connections between evidence and explanations
- recognize alternative explanations and predictions

- communicate scientific procedures and explanations
- use mathematics, where appropriate

The development of questions that are broad in scope with possibilities for exploration is central to inquiry learning. Any of the four learning contexts may serve as curriculum entry points for inquiry.

- The scientific inquiry [SI] context may be used when students want an explanation for phenomena in their natural world. When students read about solutions and dissolving rate on page 136 of *Pearson Science 7*, they may pose questions about what affects the rate of dissolving—will heat affect it? particle size? Developing testable questions is the start of the inquiry process.
- The technological problem-solving [TPS] context may be used when students wish to build something to solve a practical human problem. Reading about densities in *Pearson Science 8* may lead students to wonder if there is a simple way to measure density using common materials. Students can solve this "problem" by building and testing a hydrometer.
- The STSE decision-making [DM] context may be used when students inquire about an issue that has scientific, technological, societal, or environmental connections. Topics such as electricity generation, human activities in ecosystems, and safe drinking water all have STSE links that students may wish to investigate further. What effects do electricity generating stations have on the environment? What are the costs associated with obtaining safe drinking water in different areas of the world? What are the benefits and drawbacks of technologies that help us to reduce, reuse, and recycle?
- The cultural perspective [CP] context of the profile of Traditional Knowledge Keeper Judy Bear, p. 41 of *Pearson Science 6* may lead students to questions of their personal stewardship of Earth and its resources; preliminary discussion, reflection, and revision of ideas may lead to new and more precise questions or applications.

The *Pearson Science Program* provides a model of a specific type of Inquiry Process of Science — a systematic empirical inquiry process. This inquiry process can be found at the back of the student texts in Toolkit 2. Note that this is only one form that the inquiry process might take. A more generic form of the cyclical process of inquiry is illustrated below.

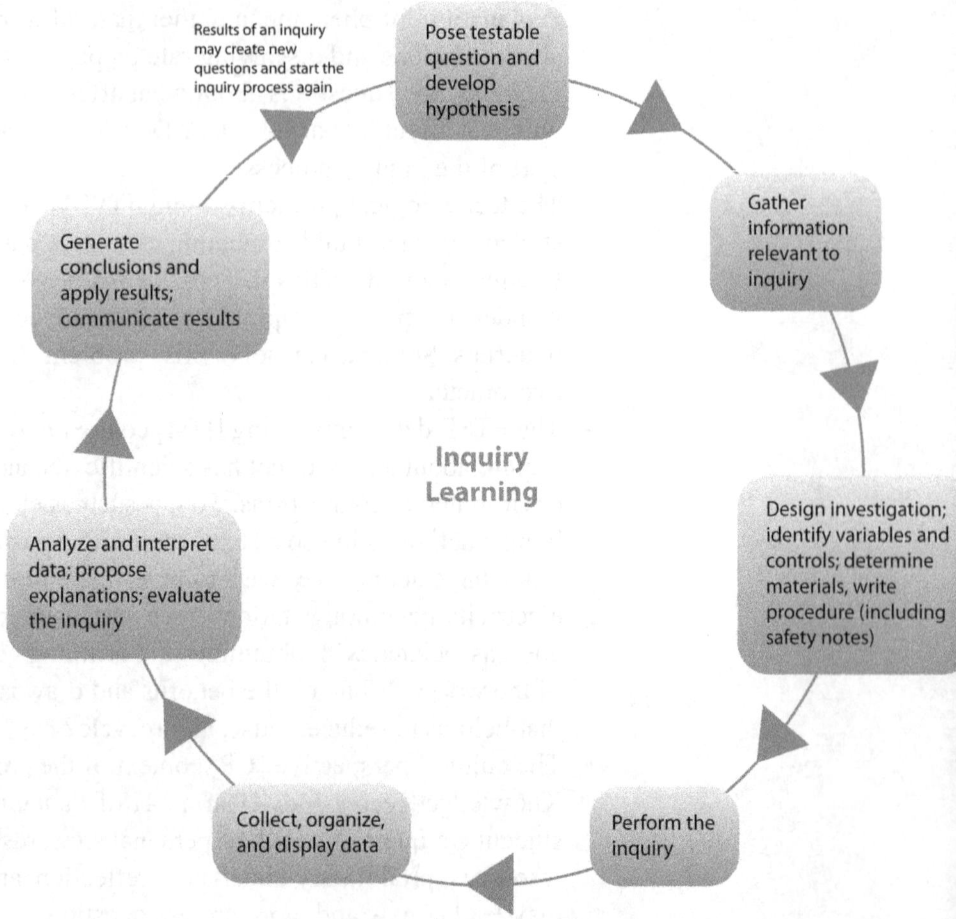

The Problem-Solving Process for Technological Development

It's easy to confuse technology with science since many of the applications of each are closely related. However, important differences exist between science and technology.

In Science...	In Technology...
we inquire about nature	we design solutions to problems of human needs
we design solutions to problems of human needs	we build something and test it out
we narrow down an investigation to find out the answer to one question	we broaden the design process to creatively come up with a variety of solutions
we should always get the same answer to the same question if we carefully control the variables	we may find many different solutions and designs that solve the same problem

Pearson Science 6–8 student books provide one example of a problem-solving process for technological development based on several steps. See Toolkit 3 in the student editions for more details on the process. A more generic form of the iterative problem-solving process is illustrated below.

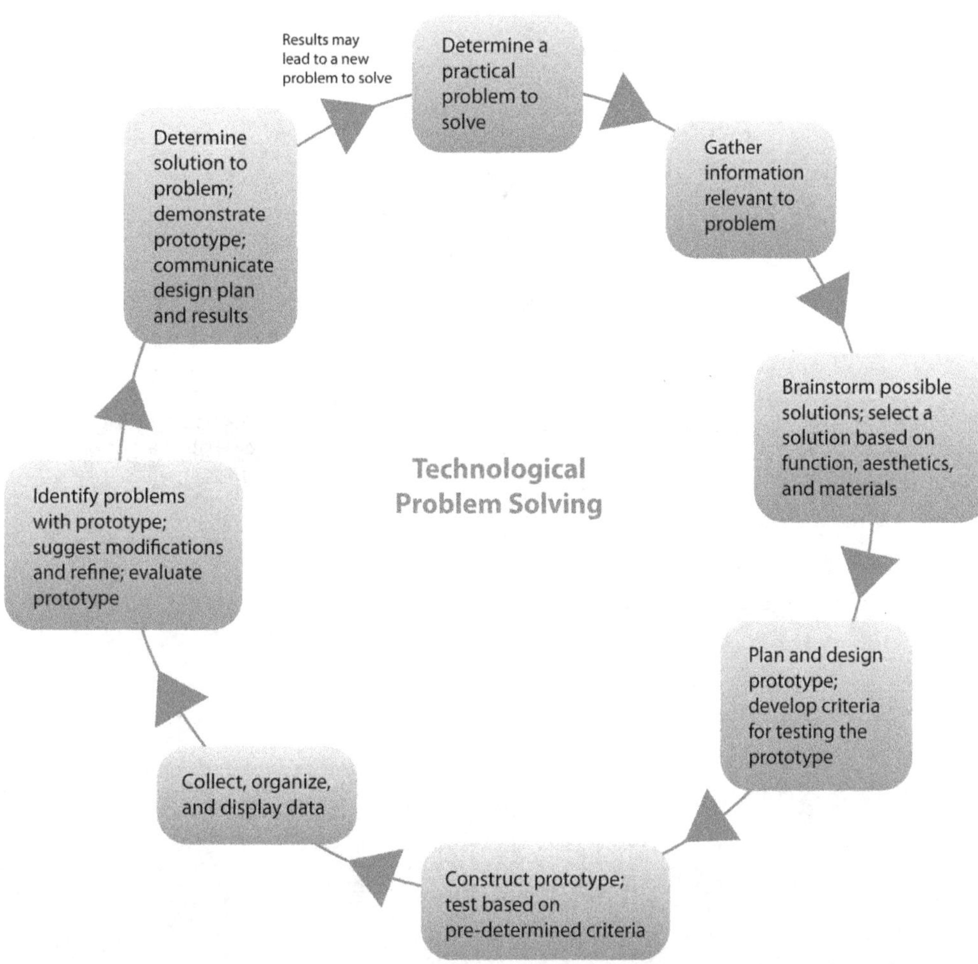

The Decision-Making Process for STSE

Scientific knowledge can relate to understanding the connections among science, technology, society, and the environment. Students need to be able to critically assess information and to see the viewpoints of different stakeholders.

Pearson Science 6–8 student books provide one example of a decision-making process based on several steps. See Toolkit 4 in the student editions for more details on the process. A more generic form of the decision-making process is illustrated below.

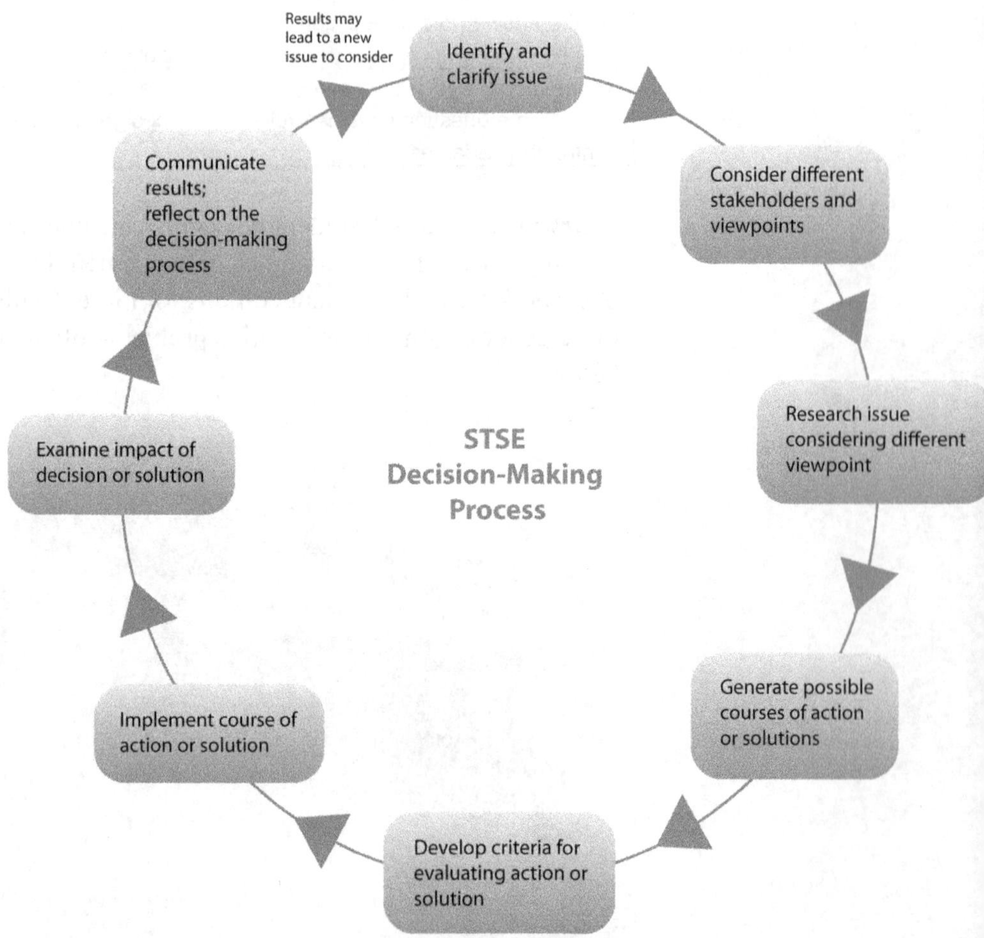

Purposeful Activities and Features – Learning Contexts

Each feature in the *Pearson Science Program* supports an aspect of the goals of science and technology and the development of scientifically and technologically literate students. Activities will occur through one or more of the four learning contexts: scientific inquiry [SI]; technological problem solving [TPS]; STSE decision making [DM]; and cultural perspectives [CP].

Pearson Science 6

- The Big Ideas at the beginning of a unit are summary statements of major concepts encompassing the central ideas of the curriculum. Specific indicators from the curriculum are addressed within the corresponding unit of *Pearson Science 6.*
- **Get Started** provides introductory information about the topic, usually complemented by a large, striking visual. Concepts may be developed further under individual subheadings, leading to Work On It activities.
- **Work On It** activities are often short, informal activities used to engage students. These activities are related to the outcomes and indicators listed in the Saskatchewan Science curriculum.
  - Some **Work On It** activities are inquiry activities that provide students with the opportunity to work in a formal laboratory-like setting. Students develop skills stressed through the learning context of scientific inquiry [SI]. (See pages 31–33 of the student book.)
  - Some **Work On It** activities are design and build challenges that provide opportunities to solve practical problems that arise from human needs or wants. Usually, students build a device or system to solve a problem through the learning context of technological problem solving [TPS]. (See pages 124–125 of the student book.)
  - Some **Work On It** activities are mainly reading and analysis of information. They may involve students in exploration of the social, economic, environmental, political, ethical, and moral impacts of a real-world issue related to the unit being studied. These activities will occur through the learning context/s of STSE decision making and/or cultural perspectives [DM, CP]. (See page 106 of the student book.)
  - Some **Work On It** activities involve new information discovered as part of the Work On It process. These activities help the student to develop his/her new knowledge. These activities will occur through the learning context/s of scientific inquiry and/or technological problem solving [SI, TPS]. (See pages 195–196 of the student book.)
- Safety is emphasized throughout.

- **Think Again!** This feature provides extra depth on a topic or develops a concept investigated in the Work On It activity. For example, on pages 164–165 the Think again! discussion highlights the effect of different wing shapes in nature, after students have created "wings" of various shapes.
- **Communicate** activities allow students to stop and consider information they have read or the activity they have just completed.
- **! box** margin items give students additional information or interesting facts on topics discussed in the text.
- **Try This at Home** provides safe, simple activities that students could carry out at home to extend their understanding of a topic.

Pearson Science 7* and *Pearson Science 8

- The **Big Idea** headings are summary statements describing major concepts in a particular section. These summary statements encompass the outcomes and indicators of the curriculum. The **Big Idea** is a key concept that the student should remember after completing the unit.
- **Invitation to Explore** activities provide real-world examples at the beginning of each unit. They allow students to draw on what they know, share their ideas about a topic, and ask questions related to the unit. The short **Problem Solver** activity that follows asks students to solve a particular problem and use information from their prior knowledge.
- **Focus Your Thoughts** encourages students to draw conclusions from their initial exploration.
- The **Explore, Develop**, and **Communicate** icons in each numbered section emphasize the constructivist approach to the presentation of the content.
- **Check Your Progress** sections at the end of each Big Idea allow students to review their development of understanding of key concepts in the unit.
- **Investigator** inquiry activities in the text provide students with the opportunity to work in a formal laboratory setting so they can develop skills of Initiating and Planning, Performing and Recording, Analyzing and Interpreting, and Communication and Teamwork through the learning context of scientific inquiry [SI] as discussed in the Saskatchewan Science curriculum documents. (See pages 150–151 of *Pearson Science 7*.)
- **Problem Solver** activities in *Pearson Science 7* provide students with open-ended activities to solve practical problems through creative thinking. Students may build a device or system to solve a problem. These activities are further elaborated as **Technological Problem Solver** activities in *Pearson Science* 8. All these activities occur through the learning context of technological problem solving [TPS]. (See page 260 of *Pearson Science 7*.)

- **Decision Maker** activities have students explore the social, economic, environmental, political, ethical, and moral impacts of a real-world issue related to the unit being studied. Students develop an opinion and make a decision based on evidence. These activities occur through the learning context of STSE decision making and/or cultural perspectives [DM, CP]. (See page 326 of *Pearson Science 7*.)
- **Experiment on Your Own** activities are either scientific inquiry or problem-solving in nature. They give students a chance to make hypotheses and design their own experiment, controlling variables appropriately. These activities occur through the learning context of scientific inquiry [SI] or technological problem solving [TPS]. (See page 63 of *Pearson Science 7*.)
- Safety is emphasized throughout.
- Bolded terms are defined in the running text and referenced in the Glossary.
- **reSEARCH** is usually a Web-based research feature designed to link student learning with the real world.
- **infoBITs** provide interesting facts or unusual ideas related to the concepts in the unit.
- **Try This at Home** provides safe, simple activities that students could carry out at home to extend their understanding of a topic.
- **Science World** presents issues, historical information, interesting current events, and possible future innovations that are related to the topics in the unit. Students are asked to express their opinion.
- The **Unit Project** challenges students to use various skills, depending on the unit of study and the skills practised throughout the unit.

The Process Skills of Science

The *Pearson Science Program* provides students with opportunities to explore the world around them and investigate questions through hands-on activities. As students engage in these activities and investigations, they develop and acquire the following process skills that form the foundation of scientific inquiry.

Observe: use the senses to gather information

Measure: describe length, width, capacity, mass, volume, speed, and temperature of objects

Compare: identify similarities and differences

Classify: sort objects, events, or conditions according to predetermined criteria

Seriate: put objects, events, or conditions in a logical sequence

Communicate: exchange ideas, knowledge, and questions through speaking, writing, presenting, listening, viewing, and reading

Infer: make assumptions based on reasoning

Predict: make decisions about what may happen based on first-hand experience or observations

Hypothesize: use observations and inferences to formulate possible explanations

Experiment/Investigate: plan and carry out investigations to test predictions or hypotheses

Controlling Variables: manipulate conditions to determine the effect of those conditions on the result of an experiment

Interpret: use collected information to draw conclusions

Making Models: represent objects by constructing replicas of them from different materials

Question: pose a question and research its answer

Use Numbers: use math skills to analyze data and/or graphs

Summarize: explain results in your own words

Skills Toolkits

This essential feature provides students with reference material they will need to be successful in the course, including lab safety, scientific and mathematical skills, and different kinds of investigative skills:

Toolkit 1: Safety Symbols
Toolkit 2: The Inquiry Process of Science
Toolkit 3: The Problem-Solving Process for Technological Development
Toolkit 4: The Decision-Making Process for Social and Environmental Issues
Toolkit 5: Reading in Science (grades 6 and 7); Researching Topics (grade 8)
Toolkit 6: Communicating in Science (grades 6 and 7); Reading in Science (grade 8)
Toolkit 7: Measurement (grades 6 and 7); Communicating in Science (grade 8)
Toolkit 8: Graphing (grade 7) Measurement (grade 8)
Toolkit 9: Graphing (grade 8)
Toolkit 10: Using a Microscope

Toolkit 1 is essential, as safety is central to learning science. Toolkits 2, 3, and 4 provide possible sequences for the Inquiry process in science, the Problem-solving process in technology, and the Decision-making process for social and environmental issues. Reading in Science and Communicating in Science, along with the literacy activities found throughout the text, will assist students in learning how to read, interpret, and write about the rich information associated with studying science. Mathematical skills are essential to being successful in science. The sections on measurement and graphing provide help with these skills. Toolkit 10 in *Pearson Science 8* gives the essential steps for using a microscope correctly.

4 Helping Students Relate Science and Technology to the World Outside the School

Overview

There are many ways to help students see "real-life" applications of science in the world outside the classroom. One of these is through field trips, be it to a natural environment such as a pond or park, or to a facility such as a factory, museum, or science centre. Most school divisions have instituted rules concerning field trips, which should be followed. Additionally, it is crucial that the purpose of the trip be fully understood by the students before the trip; that the students have specific information to obtain, or questions to research.

Another way to relate science to the "world outside" is to have guests who are involved in some aspect of science as part of their career or hobby speak to the class. First Nations or Métis Elders and Traditional Knowledge Keepers may be invited into the classroom to share their wisdom on particular topics. Teachers should follow the appropriate protocol in contacting Elders and Traditional Knowledge Keepers (see below). Again, any division policies or guidelines about classroom visitors should be followed, and students should be responsible for preparing appropriate questions beforehand and thanking the visitor at the end.

Protocol for Contacting Elders and Traditional Knowledge Keepers

For most First Nations and Métis groups, transmission of knowledge (teaching) involves respect for that knowledge and its keeper. Often the teaching is given to anyone who asks and respects the protocol of the person being asked, but some knowledge is restricted and conditionally given only to a chosen few. Based on these practices, students (and teachers) need to understand a few basic rules of protocol (etiquette) in asking an Elder or Knowledge Keeper for help. The following is protocol to observe when asking an Elder or Knowledge Keeper for cultural or traditional knowledge.

1) Ask about protocol. Often it is wise to ask Elders about the protocols they use. They know that because you are not from their communities, you may not be familiar with their customs. They would be more than happy to explain those protocols.

2) Bring an appropriate gift or offering. When one approaches an Elder, a Knowledge Keeper, or anyone who follows the Traditional path, one needs to bring an appropriate gift or offering. For many First Nations and Métis people, Tobacco is appropriate. Tobacco has been

used for many generations as a type of offering. Many, if not all, First Nations and Métis people feel that Tobacco is offered as a sign of respect. The amount of Tobacco need not be significant. It can be as little as a single cigarette. Jams and tea are offered in some communities (e.g., Air Ronge). The act of giving a gift or offering comes from the value of reciprocity — the belief in the act of giving and taking. Many First Nations and Métis groups practise this value since they believe that a teaching that is earned is valued much more than one that is gratuitously given. Often in ceremony, when an Elder or any practitioner asks the Creator for help, he or she gives Tobacco. Traditional drummers will offer Tobacco to the Spirit in the animal who gave its life to make their drums.

The Elder or Knowledge Keeper will often consider one's request before answering. Give the Elder time to reflect. If the Elder is able to help, he or she will keep your Tobacco. If he or she returns the Tobacco, the Elder cannot fulfill your request. Follow up the presentation of the offering with a handshake.

3) Listen carefully. If the request is granted, the answer one gets may teach through a story. Many Elders or Knowledge Keepers use the ethic of non-interference in their teaching. They do not give the teaching directly because they want learners to reflect and to discern the knowledge for themselves.

4) Pay for their costs. If you invite an Elder or Knowledge Keeper to your classroom, remember to offer gas money and an honorarium for their time, or if possible, please arrange for transportation. Many Elders are aged, and many do not drive a vehicle.

5) Be hospitable. Offer tea (customary for many First Nations and Métis groups) and something to eat.

Things to avoid:

- One might call to arrange a visit with an Elder or Knowledge Keeper, but offer the Tobacco in person and receive the teaching face to face. Never ask for the teaching directly on the phone. It is too impersonal.
- Learning from an Elder or Knowledge Keeper requires relationship building. Please be accepting if the Elder refuses or can't fulfill your request. Some teachings are only given if the Elder feels that you are allowed to have that knowledge. For example, men may not ask women Elders for teachings on women and reproduction.
- Listen to what Elders or Knowledge Keepers do not say as much as to what they do say. If they seem to avoid a specific topic, there is a reason. They will not likely tell you the reason. It is for the listener to figure out or just accept.
- Teachers may wish to contact their division offices. Some divisions have Aboriginal co-ordinators who may already have resources at their disposal and contact with Elders or Knowledge Keepers. The office of the Treaty Commissioner retains a list of Elders who may wish to come and present to your classroom.

Cultural Perspectives

When teaching science, it is important to recognize that the cultural and religious backgrounds of students can often affect their perceptions. The students in today's Canadian classrooms are like threads woven together to create a multicultural social fabric. Each thread is unique and special. You should recognize that when science curriculum intersects with personal or family values, ethnic or cultural heritage, or religious traditions and beliefs, each student will have a unique response.

Rather than keeping science and personal values separate in the classroom, you can encourage students to explore their beliefs that pertain to science. You should encourage students to integrate their traditions or beliefs with points covered in the curriculum. In researching beliefs that pertain to their own traditions or those in a tradition with which they are less familiar, students are given the opportunity to gain a deeper appreciation of how science is an evolving discipline that exists in conversation with, and not in isolation from, other areas of human existence. **It is crucial for students to realize that their personal beliefs are respected, though these beliefs may differ from Western science perspectives.** Students can interview parents, grandparents, First Nations or Métis Elders, priests, pastors, or other religious and cultural leaders and present their findings to the class. Students lacking any particular belief system may wish to choose a religion or culture to research. Some important values that might emerge from this research include:

- stories describing the cause of a particular aspect of the environment, such as the stars, rainbows, animal adaptations, or the creation of Earth
- belief in a higher supernatural force controlling the universe
- the concept that humans are stewards of Earth and responsible for it
- belief in the unity or oneness of all things

Values such as these are particularly important in helping students feel connected to and responsible for the environment, and in realizing that they can become scientists while preserving religious and cultural beliefs. This goal is especially important vis-à-vis First Nations and Métis students. By facilitating such discussion, teachers afford classmates of First Nations and Métis students the opportunity to learn about First Nations and Métis traditions and culture. By encouraging these discussions, research, and interviews, First Nations and Métis students may feel that their cultural identities are respected, and thus, pride in their heritage is supported.

"Theories of science are continually being tested, modified, and improved as new knowledge and theories supersede existing ones."
–Pan-Canadian Protocol for Collaboration on School Curriculum K–12, 1997

"...science offers frameworks for explanations and control, which while also limited in scope, have been shown to possess particular explanatory power and which have thus become accepted by the scientific community and by society as a whole."
–Science Council of Canada, 1984

Encompassing Indigenous Perspectives in Teaching Science

The debate continues as to whether Eurocentric science can somehow coexist with Indigenous worldviews. The term "science education" in Western culture has no meaning in many Indigenous societies. Instead, other terms have been used to describe this realm: the "traditional ways of knowing," the "old knowledge," and the "cultural teachings." The recognition of differences between the Indigenous perspective and Eurocentric viewpoint of science has influenced educators to examine the nature of Eurocentric science and its effects on Indigenous students' learning and attitudes, as Indigenous and scientific perspectives often seem to differ in terms of the social goals that are achieved. Historically, the Indigenous ways of knowing and sharing (scientific) knowledge are applied to ensure survival, whereas the Eurocentric perspective promotes gaining scientific/technological knowledge for the sake of knowing, and to exert power over nature and humans. The Indigenous view of coexisting with nature and celebrating its mysteries is juxtaposed with the Eurocentric scientific view and the need to explore and define everything in its path.

Indigenous individuals, as they are discussed in the *Pearson Science Program,* are denoted as First Nations and Métis peoples. This term encompasses a broader understanding of the unique traits, identities, cultural practices, and languages of Saskatchewan's various First Nations and Métis groups. In Saskatchewan, the term "First Nations and Métis" denotes various language groups and their respective dialects. The diverse language groups represented are the Dené, Métis, Cree (plains and northern), Ojibwe (Salteaux), Lakota, Dakota, and Nakota. The *Pearson Science Program* textbooks aim at inclusion of all these voices. During the writing process, one Elder or Traditional Knowledge Keeper from a representative group was selected to be featured in each "Ask an Elder" profile, though not all the Siouan dialects (Lakota and Nakota) were represented.

Teachers must be cognizant that First Nations and Métis ways of knowing have many implications for the classroom. The *Pearson Science Program* will enable teachers with varying ranges of knowledge about First Nations and Métis ways of knowing to achieve those outcomes and indicators. Moreover, the inclusion of First Nations and Métis content comes at a time when numbers of First Nations and Métis students are on the rise. With a greater percentage of First Nations and Métis students in the classroom, teachers are encouraged to empower these students through the exploration of their traditional knowledge, attitudes, values, and beliefs.

Teachings on beliefs such as Spirit from First Nations and Métis perspectives, unquantifiable in scientific terms yet integral to their ways of knowing, cannot be divorced from the content but yet must be respected. Though these beliefs may be different from yours, and that of Eurocentric science, the aim is to enrich all students, not only First Nations and Métis, and make all students aware of other cultural perspectives. Though the textbooks specifically highlight First Nations and Métis teachings, exploration of various other cultural practices may be a benefit to all students. Lastly, significant attitudes toward the natural world can be imparted through rich dialogue, and the perspectives highlighted in these textbooks and profiles. Though scientists and adherents to the Eurocentric science perspective may disagree with the spiritual beliefs in Traditional Knowledge and repudiate their "unscientific" way of understanding certain natural phenomena, it is difficult to object to the many values contained within Indigenous knowledge.

Values such as stewardship, responsibility, interconnectedness, and interdependence of humanity and the natural world abound in traditional legends and teachings but are also part of the science curriculum. Such values foster a love of learning and respect for nature. Our aim as educators isn't only to foster scientific literacy but it is also to engender the development of responsible, caring, scientifically literate citizens. Encouraging students to understand the world from another people's perspective allows the development of tolerance and empathy and thus strives toward this conclusion.

The Indigenous worldview has long promoted keen observation, and a knowledge and understanding of structures and designs, plants, celestial bodies, and ecological practices. Indigenous people still relay the Traditional Knowledge and teachings of their ancestors, and view this as a necessary means to ensure survival of their cultures and traditions. At the same time, it will be necessary to have competence in science to successfully participate in this highly technological society. As First Nations communities continue to grow, new scientific approaches/competencies may be realized by combining traditional ways with the new tools of science and technology to manage their environment and to promote economic growth into the next millennium. As educators, we can show not only things that are but also things that could be.

Plural or Singular?

The decision to write "Indigenous peoples" or "Indigenous people" is important from an Indigenous perspective, as evidenced by a decade-long emotional battle in the United Nations over adding an "s" to a committee's name: the "Committee on Indigenous Peoples." The use of the plural or singular depends on context, which is not always clear-cut. In a more formal context, the plural form recognizes the cultural heterogeneity among these diverse groups, and signifies an anti-stereotyping message; for example:

"Saskatchewan is home to First Nations and Métis peoples."

"First Nations and Métis peoples have their own knowledge of nature."

"During her visit to Canada, the Queen visited First Nations peoples."

This usage expresses the dignity of peoplehood of each single group. On the other hand, the singular form is appropriate when referring more informally to what people do or think, with an emphasis on individuals; for example:

"First Nations and Métis people want the best education for their children."

"I planned my science lesson with First Nations and Métis people."

"Queen Elizabeth learned to ride a dogsled during a visit with First Nations people."

It is appropriate to write, "Indigenous peoples worldwide have their own values," as well as "Indigenous people in my community have their own values." On a related topic, the phrase "First Nations" never has an apostrophe associated with it, even in the possessive case (e.g., "First Nations ways of thinking"); and it is always plural except when mentioning one specific nation, as in "Richard is from the Ojibwe First Nation." And lastly, "First Nations," "Aboriginal," and "Indigenous" are capitalized to dignify their recognition.

References

D. Peat, *Lighting the Seventh Fire*. New York: Carol Publishing Group, 1994.

W.J. Ermine, *First Nations Education in Canada: The Circle Unfolds.* Vancouver: UBC Press, 1995.

G. Allen and O. Sewptewa, National Science Teachers Association Journal (1994): 41.

Two Ways of Knowing Nature

by Glen Aikenhead

Two broadly different knowledge systems – scientific and Indigenous – can help us understand and deal with our physical world. They do not contradict each other, but can complement each other. They have similarities, differences, strengths, and limitations.

A fundamental similarity is that they are both anchored in a cultural milieu from which they originated and are currently sustained. Scientific ways of knowing nature arose and flourish within Euro-American cultures and largely portray a Eurocentric worldview. To function as a scientist, one must conduct oneself professionally in science's Eurocentric way. Similarly, Indigenous ways of knowing nature portray Indigenous worldviews. Moreover, both knowledge systems are systematically empirical, communal, continually revisable, rational, valid, and responsible for consequences generally valued by the cultural communities they serve.

Their differences arise from their respective worldviews. Science limits itself to the physical world, while Indigenous knowledge integrates the physical and metaphysical, which includes spirituality, among other things. Thus, the two knowledge systems are rational but in different common-sense ways. Although they are both empirically based, science emphasizes measurable data collected in relatively short periods of time, while Indigenous knowledge draws upon both observable and intuitive metaphysical data. Because Indigenous "experiments" are based on natural changes in the local environment, they can take several generations to complete.

Science is communal and revisable because communities of scientists work toward producing agreed-upon representations of the physical world, sometimes called "scientific truth." These representations can change with new data or new ideas, if agreed upon by scientists through argument-based processes of consensus making (e.g., peer review) and if recorded in writing. On the other hand, Indigenous knowledge is orally and experientially passed down intergenerationally (e.g., through community activities, stories, dances, and other art forms) and is modified as experience dictates. Elders' ways of being in Mother Earth are a combination of accumulated wisdom and current local circumstances that need action to be taken for the community's survival in the physical and metaphysical world. This is sometimes called "wisdom in action." One contrast here is between intellectual representations that students can explore, describe, and memorize, and students learning to live wisely in nature. In short, science provides an intellectual view of the physical world while Indigenous knowledge concerns wise ways of being in Mother Earth (the physical and metaphysical world).

The way scientists see nature can appear to clash with the way Indigenous Elders inhabit nature. One way to acknowledge this difference is to appreciate the culture clashes that many Aboriginal students experience in school science, clashes between their own culture and the culture of science, which is embedded in science instruction. Worldview values and assumptions embraced by science can conflict with students' cultural views of the world.

Each knowledge system has particular strengths, but strengths can also be limitations. The holistic wisdom tradition of Indigenous knowledge is necessarily so complex that precise predictions rarely occur consistently in the short term. But in many fields of science, making accurate predictions is a strength. Experimental designs must be rigorous, results of experiments must be reproducible, and field studies must be replicated a sufficient number of times. This is accomplished by following a reductionist approach to inquiry in which scientists analytically reduce a complex phenomenon into simpler parts or variables amenable to measurement, conceptualization, and experimentation. Scientists assume that the "whole" can then be understood by putting together its parts. From an Indigenous worldview perspective, however, scientific reductionism is a severe limitation to knowing nature because it ignores a holistic understanding of the physical world, in which individual parts have meaning only in terms of their interrelationships with the whole of creation. Indigenous knowledge (wisdom in action) focusses on relationships among knowledge, people, and all of creation. Mother Earth is a web of interrelationships and the responsibilities that accompany each relationship.

Indigenous knowledge has proven its validity over tens of thousands of years through the survival of Indigenous people in extreme circumstances where harmony with nature pays off. Science has not been in existence long enough to test its validity with respect to human survival on planet Earth over a long span of time. But the validity of science with respect to its power over nature and its contribution to material progress is unquestionable.

Unlike the generalizable type of knowledge sought by science, Indigenous knowledge is place based; its validity does not extend beyond the local environment inhabited by the people who hold that knowledge and whose cultural identity is intimately defined by that place. Place-based knowledge is intuitively sensitive to unique features of local phenomena (e.g., animal behaviour and river phenomena). Such unique features can be overlooked by scientists searching for quantifiable and generalizable patterns.

This is why some companies and government agencies employ Elders to join a team of scientists looking into issues of resource management, or the environmental impact of such developments as a new pipeline or mine. Scientists learn "Traditional Ecological Knowledge" (TEK) from the Elders on the team. This knowledge can be helpful to the company's or agency's decision on what to do. However, the Elders do not make the final decision. Sometimes they feel that their TEK is not understood adequately when a decision goes against their way of understanding the impact of a decision.

Depending on their field of study, scientists conduct investigations using a variety of agreed-upon methods. The diversity within science is great. However, experimental scientists conform to such values as being honest and conscientious about the rigour of their experimental procedures, and being open to submitting their results for peer review, whenever possible. An acceptable result must be reproducible and must significantly add to scientists' knowledge of their field. There is also great diversity among Indigenous peoples that no one worldview can speak for all nations. Local variations are a part of a people's identity.

In summary, Indigenous knowledge is place based, holistic, relational, spiritual, systematically empirical, continually revisable, rational, valid, and communal. It integrates the metaphysical and physical into one interrelated whole in which Spirit flows through relationships and responsibilities.

The Worldview of the Sweetgrass Cree First Nation

The worldview diagram of the Sweetgrass Cree people created by Traditional Knowledge Keeper Judy Bear has been included for your information on page PO-67. This diagram, as authorized by her Elders, depicts the worldview of her people although it is general enough to extend to other First Nations groups. A detailed discussion is also included based on an interview with her on February 10th 2010. For Judy Bear it is crucial that teachers appreciate the key aspects of a traditional worldview and she feels that certain nuances may be lost upon a reader without a detailed discussion. Therefore, key terms such as "traditional knowledge," "traditional knowledge keeper," and "worldview" have been defined.

Defining Traditional Knowledge and Traditional Knowledge Keeper

First Nations peoples of Saskatchewan learned long ago how they fit into the natural world and its cycles. They adapted to the land instead of altering the land to accommodate them and their needs (Judy Bear, 2010). That understanding has survived for millennia, passed down from generation to generation through oral tradition, and has become a keystone to a venerable way of life.

To understand that way of life, we must first define "*traditional knowledge*." Judy Bear (2010) teaches that "traditional knowledge is imparted at a very early age. Traditional knowledge involves the living of experiences such as ceremonies, the hearing of the stories, and the messages within them told to them by grandparents and other traditional people. Finally, that traditional knowledge includes the act of passing down that knowledge, as it is recalled and transmitted through oral tradition." Thus, to be a Traditional Knowledge Keeper is to be a person who lives by the ideals of the culture, preserving the knowledge and passing it down to subsequent generations.

Understanding Traditional Worldview

A careful look at the integral components of traditional knowledge further elucidates our understanding of traditional worldview. Although many First Nations and Métis peoples have distinct cultural practices, languages, customs, protocols, and ceremonies, their cultures share many elements that help inform a generalized traditional worldview.

For many First Nations and Métis peoples, a worldview is more than simply a way of looking at the natural world; it is a belief system that encompasses relationships with Mother Earth, one's surroundings, and the things therein, but above all, worldview includes a relationship to the Creator. Worldview includes the experiences, practices, and ceremonies of that particular people. The person is immersed in the beliefs and the values through ceremonies, language, and customs. Beliefs about the land and their relationship to Mother Earth and the Creator become so natural that they permeate the actions, the ceremonies, the daily life, and the language of that people (Judy Bear, 2010).

Another key component of worldview common to most First Nations and Métis people is the belief in the element of spirit. Objects, which scientists would class as non-living such as rocks and fire, are in fact animate and are imbued with that very spirit. Spirituality plays such an important role in the Cree culture for example, that even their language, and its suffixes and prefixes possess exact spiritual connotation (Judy Bear, 2010).

The Worldview Diagram of the Sweetgrass Cree People Explained

The diagram entitled "The Worldview of the Sweetgrass Cree People" was a project done by Traditional Knowledge Keeper Judy Bear. It contains beliefs and ideas given to her and authorized by her Elders.

Cree oral tradition provides an explanation for the sequence and order of living things within the worldview diagram. Although the Cree believe that all things were created equally, life, as it unfolds, is not. This diagram helps teachers understand the general worldview of the Sweetgrass Cree people.

The diagram's most important piece, the "Creator," is situated at the very top. For many Cree, to define the Creator is unnecessary. For them, that the Creator is the creative force from which all things come is enough. For Judy Bear "... it is enough to look around Mother Earth to see the Creator in the grass and the butterflies." (Judy Bear, 2010) On the next tier below the Creator, we find Earth, Sun, Moon, and Stars. The Cree refer to Earth as "Mother Earth," for they liken Earth to a mother who nourishes and provides her children with everything they need for survival. The sacred elements of wind, water, fire, and rock extend from Earth. Under Earth in the diagram, we find plants. Plant life holds a very important place within the Cree belief system since plant life provides everything that humans need to survive. Plant life affords food, shelter, and substances for healing. Moreover, some plants are considered sacred and are employed in ceremonies. Four main plants are revered: Tobacco, Sage, Sweetgrass, and Cedar.

Tobacco, as it is known and commonly used for recreational smoking and often associated with lung cancer, is not the sacred plant mixture that was used in many Cree ceremonies. Hundreds of years ago, instead of tobacco, a plant mixture called *Ciscēmās* [chis-shay-mas], made from dried bearberry leaves and other sacred plants, was used. This mixture was employed in pipe ceremonies. Through trade, tobacco was obtained and used (Judy Bear, 2010). The borrowed word "*tobacco*" was used as the English equivalent to denote the Cree word Ciscēmās.

In the diagram, below plant life, small life forms, water and sky life, and land life (four- and two-legged) follow, respectively. Small life forms are living things that hop, burrow, and crawl (Judy Bear, 2010) such as insects and earthworms. Water life includes all aquatic life forms such as fish, frogs, and turtles, while birds, such as eagles, hawks, and owls make up the sky life. Land life includes both four-legged and two-legged beings. The four-leggeds like elk, buffalo, deer, and moose provide meat, shelter, and clothing. Last, we find the two-leggeds—humanity (Judy Bear, 2010).

There are many lessons that this diagram can teach us about our relationship with Earth. This worldview challenges the traditional Eurocentric view that Earth is to be used and its resources exploited. Many First Nations and Métis peoples may argue that stewardship is the only way to preserve the remaining natural world and though humans may need resources from the land, they mustn't destroy Earth in that pursuit. "Take only what is needed and give back" is the adage by which the First Nations have lived for countless millennia. The offering of Tobacco is an expression of this belief and a practice of the value of reciprocity.

This way of looking at the natural world imparts a wisdom passed down for many generations. It teaches its adherents to value Earth, to respect it, and to live harmoniously within it. In short, the diagram illustrates a way of life that is sustainable.

First Nations Historical Worldview

Tāpwēwakēyihtamōwin-pimātisiwin-cycle of life

"As long as the sun shines, the grass grows and the water flows"

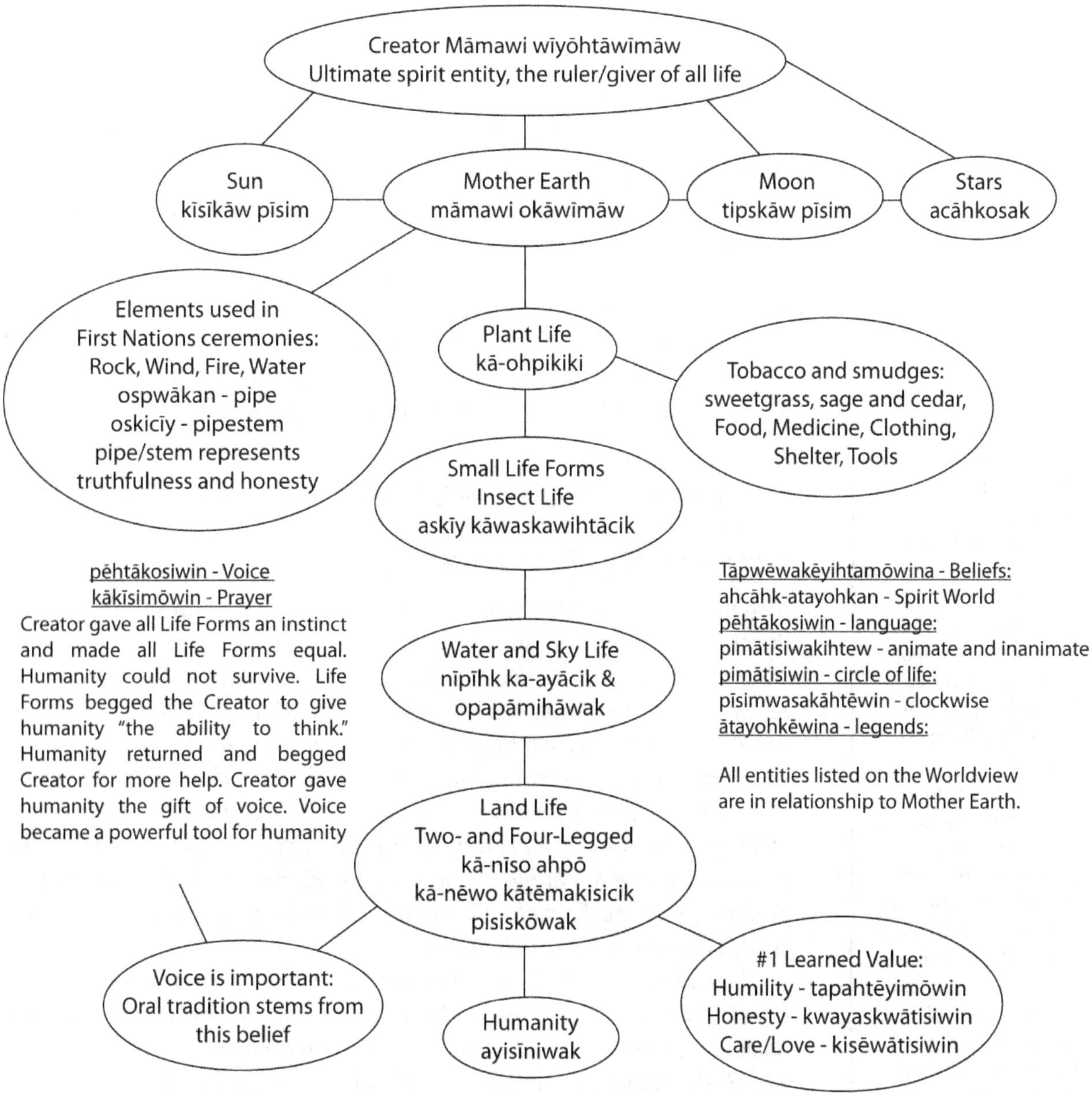

Traditional teaching — learning takes place before birth:
The mother shapes the unborn child's emotions, transfers feelings such as Love, Caring and Compassion.
Each part in this Worldview is a Teaching.

Written by Judy Bear, sanctioned by her consultant Elders
Based on the First Nations People oral traditions.
Used with permission.

Helping Students Appreciate the Need for Sustainable Development

What Is Sustainable Development?

In 1987, the Brundtland Commission, a United Nations organization charged with the task of taking an in-depth look at our planet's people and resources, defined sustainable development as "development that meets the needs of the present without compromising the ability of future generations to meet their own needs." Sustainable development is also commonly defined as development that has a beneficial effect on the *environment, human well-being,* and the *economy.* In any sustainable decision, all three of these factors must be considered and balanced.

A sustainable community should:
- provide and maintain human equality, freedom, and general well-being
- protect human health
- maintain biodiversity and ecosystems
- prevent and repair environmental damage
- use renewable and non-renewable resources efficiently
- have a sense of global stewardship and responsibility

In addition, a sustainable world should:
- address the growing inequality between the world's wealthy and the poor
- provide food for Earth's growing population

You may like to use the following explanation to explain sustainable development simply to students:
If we make sure all our decisions help Earth, Earth will stay healthy for us and for our children, and provide us with all we need to live. But if our decisions hurt Earth by polluting and using up too many resources, Earth will get sick. It will not be able to provide food, energy, clean water, and clean air for us and for our children. Right now, Earth is starting to get sick—plants and animals are dying. So people around the world are trying to change the way we use Earth's materials and stop polluting to make Earth healthy again. This new way of making decisions is called sustainable development.

Around the world, people are working on lots of sustainable development projects. Close to home, many initiatives are taking place in Saskatchewan to make the province more environmentally sustainable. The Saskatchewan government's "Go Green" Plan encourages homeowners and communities to make sustainable choices. It encourages recycling programs and offers financial incentives to retrofit homes to become more energy efficient. Though it officially proffers a stance on the environment, the provincial government lags with regard to Kyoto targets.

> Manitoba also has many "green" programs that help contribute to sustainable development. For more information on green initiatives in Manitoba, check the Green Manitoba website (http://greenmanitoba.ca) or the Climate and Green Initiatives website (http://www.gov.mb.ca/conservation/climate/index.html), part of the Department of Conservation and Water Stewardship of the Government of Manitoba. You may also want to talk to your local government about green initiatives.

Many communities and citizens' groups, however, have striven greatly for sustainable development. The Craik Sustainable Living Project is one such example. This initiative consists of an Eco Centre and a thriving sustainable village. The Eco Centre is entirely made from recycled materials such as timber from two old elevators, straw bales that provide insulation (R-40), used bricks, and a roof of cellulose. Passive solar radiant heating, an in-house biological water treatment facility, and solar and wind energy ensures that the centre is sustainable. Many homeowners are retrofitting their homes, through increasing the use of energy-efficient furnaces, adding insulation, and changing their appliances. Saskatchewan's SARCAN, a division of Saskatchewan Association of Rehabilitation Centres that employs people with disabilities and special needs, has added computer recycling to their current recycling program to offer people an alternative to throwing away their electronics. The Spirit Creek Watershed Monitoring Committee is a group of activists who monitor effluent from cattle operations to ensure the health of streams, lakes, and rivers.

Why Is Sustainable Development Necessary?

Human activity has damaged Earth to an alarming extent. At the present moment, almost every location and species on Earth has been touched by pollution. In the Arctic, for example, dangerously high levels of harmful chemicals have been found in every part of the food chain. Species around the world are becoming extinct at an estimated loss of anywhere from 25 to 100 species a day. If Earth's **biodiversity** is not maintained, ecosystems may become unstable and collapse.

Space for safe waste disposal is also running out, and Earth's natural resources are being strained to the limit of their ability to regenerate. The atmosphere above Earth has also been seriously disrupted. Chemicals that seep into the air from refrigerants and packing foam have diminished the protective **ozone layer**, and **greenhouse gases** that are released when we burn fossil fuels continue to pile up in the atmosphere, adding to global warming. All of these issues indicate that the current lifestyle of the human race is unsustainable and, by definition, cannot be continued indefinitely.

Another major issue of unsustainability is the gap between the rich and poor—a gap that continues to grow. Today, the richest 20% of the world's people consume about 80% of the world's income and resources. At the other end of the scale, the poorest 20% of the world's people lack the basic needs of food, sanitation, and safe drinking water.

Human wealth and poverty are both major causes of environmental degradation. Over-consumption by wealthy nations, including Canada, has led to toxic pollution around the world, global warming, and the depletion of many of Earth's natural resources. The extreme poverty of countries in Latin America, Africa, and Asia has led to **land desertification** through over-use, the destruction of rainforests, and species extinction resulting from the loss of habitats.

Canada: Sustainable or Not?

Many Canadians have a false sense of security. We feel protected from global problems by misperceived distance from them and by our country's great natural wealth. However, sustainability issues are present in Canada as well:

- In the prairie provinces, wind and water erosion leads to the loss of millions of tonnes of valuable topsoil each year.
- In eastern Canada, acid rain has damaged 150 000 out of 700 000 lakes, killing innumerable fish, amphibians, and waterfowl.
- Forests throughout Canada are being disrupted and reduced by unsustainable logging practices and pollution. The loss of these forest habitats is endangering wildlife across the country.
- Thirteen species of Canadian wildlife are extinct, 22 are no longer found in Canada, and over 565 species are endangered or threatened.
- Overfishing has caused cod to all but disappear from the ocean off Canada's east coast, and salmon have recently started to disappear from the west coast at an alarming rate.

Like all other peoples, Canadians are citizens of Earth. We influence and are influenced by global issues much more than we realize. For example, deforestation in Canada contributes to global warming by removing trees that absorb carbon dioxide, a major greenhouse gas. Our consumption leads to the continued over-use of non-renewable natural resources such as fossil fuels, which contributes to global warming. Storms and air currents carry pesticide pollution from countries all over the world. Some of this pollution ends up in Canada—notably, in the Arctic, where its effects are most dramatic among children and wildlife.

Definitions	
biodiversity	the variety of life and diversity of species on Earth
ozone layer	ozone in the stratosphere that protects life on Earth from overexposure to dangerous UV radiation
greenhouse gases	gases such as carbon dioxide, methane, and nitrous oxide that trap heat in the atmosphere
global warming	an unexpected increase in global temperature, caused by the accumulation of greenhouse gases in the atmosphere
land desertification	the conversion of fertile land into near-desert through erosion and overharvesting
CFCs	a short form for *chlorofluorocarbons,* chemicals used for refrigeration and aerosols. CFCs are known to lead to ozone depletion and are also greenhouse gases. Phase-out plan was incorporated in Montreal Protocol of 1987.

What Is Canada Doing About Sustainable Development?

The Canadian federal government has developed numerous sustainable development strategies, policies, and programs. These cover waste management, soil and water conservation, wildlife habitat conservation, forest management, and much more.

In 1987, Montreal was the site of promulgation of the Montreal Protocol on Substances that Deplete the Ozone Layer, an agreement to phase out/ limit the use of CFCs. Since the Montreal Protocol came into effect, the atmospheric concentrations of the most important chlorofluorocarbons and related chlorinated hydrocarbons have either levelled off or decreased. This protocol is often called the world's most successful international environmental agreement.

In 1997, Canada and 160 other countries negotiated the Kyoto Protocol, an agreement to reduce emissions of greenhouse gases. Canada's commitment under this protocol is to reduce emissions by 6% below the 1990 level by 2008–2012. Since then, little in the way of governmental initiatives have been made to meet the Kyoto Protocol commitment. In fact, since the signing of the Kyoto Accord, Canada's emissions have risen a frightening 30% above target goals for 2012. Judging by 2009 levels, Canada will not achieve its target goal, that of reducing CO_2 emissions by 6% below the 1990 level by the year 2012.

At the provincial level, governments have developed policies and programs to promote sustainable forestry and agricultural practices, energy efficiency, and green energy programs, and sustainability education programs. At the local level, municipalities have adopted recycling and composting programs and pesticide by-laws.

On the other side of the coin, government strategies, policies, and programs are largely statements of intent. Actual federal legislation over environmental areas such as endangered species and forestry practices is thought by many to be insufficient or lacking. Canada still faces many sustainability issues such as increased pressure on the northern boreal forests as human use for the wood and water in those areas increases, loss of habitat for species like caribou, and depletion of cod fisheries on the east coast. Increased development of the tar sands in Alberta and Saskatchewan and the rise of CO_2 emissions from those developments is an example of another threat to sustainability. Though Canada took a lead role at the outset of Kyoto talks, the nation has quickly lagged behind, becoming the third largest contributor of CO_2 per capita in the world. With current practices, Canada may not live up to its commitments. However, Canada has always taken a leadership role, globally, in environmental protection and sustainable development, and many expect Canada to remain true to our commitment.

What Can You Do?

In order for sustainable development to become a reality, our knowledge and skill base and many of society's values need to change. One national sustainability education organization, Learning for a Sustainable Future, has developed a thorough list of knowledge, skills, and values necessary for a sustainable future.

Some Suggestions for Reducing Consumption:

- Conserve paper: Write or print on the back of used sheets.
- Care for your possessions so they will last longer.
- Don't shop as a leisure activity.
- Buy only what you need.
- Buy replacements only when the original is worn out, not when you are tired of it.
- Buy second-hand clothing, furniture, and equipment.

You can encourage students to avoid overconsumption by discussing what their real needs are and why they buy the things they do. You can also foster concern and responsibility for the environment through field trips and projects in which students learn about environmental issues.

References

The Brundtland Commission, *Our Common Future*. Toronto: Oxford University Press, 1987.

M. Carley & P. Spapens, *Sharing the World: Sustainable Living and Global Equity in the 21st Century*. New York: St. Martin's Press, 1998.

M. Keating and the Canadian Global Change Program, *Canada and the State of the Planet*. Toronto: Oxford University Press, 1997.

5 Encouraging Responsible Attitudes in Science

Student Attitudes

One of the four foundations of the Pan-Canadian Common Framework of Science Learning Outcomes focusses on student attitudes toward science:

Students will be encouraged to develop attitudes that support the responsible acquisition and application of scientific and technological knowledge to the mutual benefit of self, society, and the environment.
–p. 19 Common Framework of Science Learning Outcomes

The Framework defines attitudes as "generalized aspects of behaviour that are modelled for students by example and reinforced by selective approval." In short, teachers are role models for students. It is what you do more than what you say that influences students' attitudes toward science. Through your behaviour, students will become interested in science and form positive attitudes toward it.

Most students are eager to discover how and why things work and to learn about their environment. Educators must nurture and encourage this natural curiosity and love of inquiry to develop a positive attitude to science in children. According to the Framework, "science education can contribute to attitudinal growth when…:

- students are encouraged to examine how science has an impact daily and over the long term on themselves and on the lives of others…
- students are involved in science investigations and activities that stimulate their interest and curiosity…
- students are provided with opportunities for development, reinforcement, and extension of attitudes that support scientific inquiry…
- students are provided opportunities to work in group situations on real-life problems…
- students are involved in activities that encourage responsible action toward living things and the environment and encouraged to consider issues related to sustainability from a variety of perspectives…
- students are encouraged to assess and manage potential dangers and apply safety procedures…"

The activities and sections in the *Pearson Science Program* provide several opportunities for students to develop positive attitudes toward science in all of these ways. In each unit:

- students look at how the unit science topic impacts their daily lives
- students work on thought-provoking activities and investigations designed to stimulate their curiosity
- students develop inquiry skills by formulating questions of their own and designing inquiries to investigate them

- students collaborate with partners and groups on activities and investigations
- students are encouraged to respect living things, as well as the environment, and consider sustainability issues
- students learn about safety procedures and put them in practice

Safety

When it comes to safety in the science classroom, the safety of students and teachers is a primary concern of Pearson Canada. Safety requires that you model appropriate behaviour in the laboratory, are aware of safety procedures and regulations, and provide students with safe learning environments. It is important to establish safety procedures with the class before you begin a science unit and to reinforce them on a regular basis. *Pearson Science 7 Saskatchewan Edition,* p. 99, provides a list of important Lab Safety Rules that could serve as the basis of an initial discussion of safety. This would be a good opportunity to emphasize any rules you feel are especially important and to add those that are specific to your science classroom or lab.

Throughout the *Pearson Science Program*, activities give safety instructions for the student and the teacher where appropriate. At the end of the student books, Toolkit 1 provides information on safety symbols used in the activities, on workplace-related substances (WHMIS), and on consumer products.

The following information about safety issues in the school science classroom or lab is intended to be used by classroom teachers in preparing for a lab activity and planning demonstrations. Because this is an overview, it cannot be a comprehensive coverage of everything related to school science safety. Pearson Canada takes no responsibility for the completeness of this information or for the implementation of these suggestions.

Teachers are encouraged to practise the four Ps of safety. Use the guidelines of Kwan and Texley (2003):

- **Prepare**
- Keep up to date with your personal safety knowledge and certifications.
- Be aware of national, provincial, division, and school-level safety policies and guidelines.
- Create a safety contract with students.
- **Plan**
- Develop learning plans that ensure all students learn effectively and safely.
- Choose activities that are best suited to the learning styles, maturity, and behaviour of all students and that include all students.
- Create safety checklists for in-class activities and field studies.
- **Prevent**
- Assess and mitigate hazards.

- Review procedures for accident prevention with students.
- Teach and review safety procedures with students, including the need for appropriate clothing.
- Do not use defective or unsafe equipment or procedures.
- Do not allow students to eat or drink in science areas.
- **Protect**
- Ensure students have sufficient protective devices, such as safety glasses.
- Demonstrate and instruct students on the proper use of safety equipment and protective gear.
- Model safe practice by insisting that all students, visitors, and yourself use appropriate protective devices.

The following safety suggestions are intended to help establish a program of safety awareness for staff and students.

Safe Storage of Chemicals

While most of the inquiry activities in the *Pearson Science Program* employ safe and easily available chemicals such as baking soda and vinegar, you are reminded that safety includes the safe storage of all chemical goods.

Teachers are reminded that storage of chemicals is regulated by the Hazardous Products Act. School divisions fall under this act. You must be cognizant of the Workplace Hazardous Materials Information System (WHMIS). Labels on the containers, as well as Material Safety Data Sheets (MSDSs) offer invaluable information on the safe handling, use, and storage of many chemicals. If you have to work with hazardous chemicals, you must receive training from their respective school divisions before doing so. It is the law.

- Store chemicals in stockrooms, not in the science classroom or lab.
- Do not store food in chemical refrigerators. Store chemicals only in designated chemical refrigerators.
- Do not store chemicals alphabetically. Use an approved system of chemical storage, and post legends in the stockroom.
- Store only the chemicals you will use during a school year.
- Dispose of chemicals as directed by your school or division safety committee. If you are unsure, check with your administrator.

Safety Education

- Put together a safety committee for your school. Include teachers, students, and administrators.
- Schedule regular meetings of the safety committee to discuss issues, accident reports, and the results of science classroom or lab inspections.
- Implement a safety education program for staff and students.
- Include all science department staff in safety education and assign them specific responsibilities.

- Require students to know the science safety rules; assess this by giving a safety quiz.

Safety Management

- Report all accidents to your safety committee.
- Periodically inspect science classrooms and labs and report findings to the safety committee.
- Establish an emergency plan and review it periodically with students and staff.
- Keep phone numbers for the fire department, police department, local ambulance, and poison control centre next to every phone in the science area.
- Display warning signs and safety posters.
- Prohibit student access to preparation rooms.
- Require students to keep aisles clear and counters clean. Exits should be kept free of obstacles.
- Keep a current chemical inventory. Update the chemical inventory often. Include an MSDS for each chemical. Have each MSDS easily accessible, and read those that pertain to the chemicals you use in any activity before doing the activity with students.
- Label all chemicals with the date and possible hazards. Establish a policy for buying and disposing of chemicals.
- In pre-lab discussions, stress safety issues relevant to each specific lab activity.

Safety Equipment

- Make available the following items in all science classrooms/labs and demonstration areas: an ABC fire extinguisher, a smoke alarm, a safety shower, an eyewash faucet, and a fume hood.
- Maintain and check all safety equipment regularly.
- Keep a first-aid kit stocked and available.
- Keep flammable chemicals in an approved fireproof cabinet.
- Use safety shields when there is a possibility of explosion, implosion, chemical splashing, or fire.
- Use hot plates in lieu of open flames as often as possible.
- Be prepared for mercury spills, acid spills, and other spills. Spill control devices are available from chemical suppliers.

Safety Procedures for Teachers

Although reviewing safety guidelines may be a part of your initial class, safety should be an integral part of your classroom and procedures at all times. Science and Technology teachers should always:

- Model safe practices at all times (for example, wear safety goggles and an apron, smell chemicals properly).

- Strongly discourage the wearing of contact lenses in the science room. In the event of a chemical splash into the eye, the lenses may function to hold chemicals in contact with the eye, potentially causing greater injury.
- Be able to see the whole class if working with something potentially harmful. (Don't become engrossed in a discussion with a single student.)
- Ensure all safety equipment (including first-aid kit) is available, in working order, and checked regularly. (Eyewash filters may become blocked if not checked regularly.)
- Arrange the classroom/lab furnishings so that people aren't tripping over knapsacks as they move about the room.
- Teach students the correct use of all tools and equipment before they use them.
- Use digital or non-mercury thermometers.
- Buy ample and appropriate safety equipment for the lab. (Have more than enough safety goggles. If supplying younger grades, obtain goggles in smaller sizes.)
- Dispose of broken glass in a dedicated container kept out of the way and clearly labelled.
- Dispose of batteries, oils, etc., in appropriate ways.
- Show students how to safely smell substances. Have them use their hands to waft the scent toward their noses.
- Do not encourage students to taste non-food substances.
- Label all chemicals used in experiments, even vinegar and baking soda.
- Refrain from using demonstrations that are dangerous.
- Use hot plates or microwaves instead of Bunsen burners whenever possible.
- Never leave a Bunsen burner unattended.
- Never use alcohol burners.
- Never heat flammable chemicals (e.g., alcohol) over a Bunsen burner.
- Ventilate the classroom when using or producing gases or fumes (e.g., using hot-glue guns).
- Allow hot plates time to cool off before moving them.
- Demonstrate and teach students to handle all materials safely. Use plastic containers instead of glass when applicable.
- Never use the Sun as a direct source for a light microscope.
- Store chemicals according to WHMIS standards.
- Become certified in CPR and emergency first aid.
- Smooth sharp edges of glass mirrors with duct tape.
- Be aware of student allergies (foods, plants, animals, latex, environmental) and asthma.

- Be careful of plants in the room because some students may have allergies and some plants are poisonous.
- Choose pets for your classroom carefully. Some pets carry diseases or cause allergies (see also **Living Things in the Classroom**).
- Supervise students closely when they are using electricity, heat, or chemicals. Small groups are easier to supervise than individuals or partners. Depending upon the students and the hazards involved, teacher demonstration may be the best teaching strategy to use.
- Circulate around the class to observe students, and correct procedures by demonstration if necessary.
- Have students do procedures that produce fumes, such as gluing or sanding, only in areas with adequate ventilation.

Safety Procedures for Students

In addition to becoming familiar with Toolkit 1 and using their common sense, students may need to review these safety rules/procedures:

- Know the emergency fire exit route.
- Stop, drop, and roll if your clothes catch fire.
- Become familiar with safety equipment such as fire blankets, fire extinguishers, and eyewash stations.
- Keep your work area uncluttered and organized.
- If you have long or loose hair, tie it back. Roll up long shirt sleeves.
- Don't wear any jewellery when doing laboratory experiments.
- Make your teacher aware of any safety concerns, including allergies or medical conditions.
- Follow instructions carefully.
- Always wear safety goggles and any other safety clothing as requested by your teacher.
- Do not leave any experiment unattended.
- Never smell any material or substance directly. Instead, gently wave your hand over it to bring its vapours toward your nose.
- Do not eat in the science lab.
- Do not taste chemicals unless told to do so by the teacher.
- Do not engage in horseplay in the lab.
- Direct flying devices away from yourself and other classmates.
- Never stare directly at bright light sources such as the Sun or laser pointers.
- Never work alone.
- Learn to recognize warning symbols.
- Heat solids and liquids only in heat-resistant glass beakers and test tubes.
- Heat glass containers only if they are Pyrex or Kimax.
- Never use broken or cracked glassware.
- Report broken glass or spills to the teacher immediately.

- Place test tubes in a rack when pouring chemicals into them.
- If your skin is exposed to chemicals, wash it thoroughly with water and inform the teacher.
- Do not mix substances unless you are told to do so. Many chemicals, including household products like bleach, vinegar, and ammonia, can be dangerous when mixed.
- When you heat test tubes, make sure that the open end is pointing away from you and anyone else in the room.
- If heating a substance, make sure the container does not boil dry.
- Make sure you close the containers of chemicals immediately after you use them.
- Safely dispose of all waste materials and chemicals as instructed by the teacher.
- When you have finished an experiment, clean all the equipment before putting it away.
- Be careful with hot plates and pieces of equipment that have been heated as they may take a long time to cool down.
- Always wash your hands well with soap, preferably liquid soap, after handling chemicals, soil, plants, or animals.
- Make sure that any water or wet hands are kept away from electrical outlets.

Living Things in the Classroom

Using living things in the classroom can enhance a science program and may expose students to a new experience. Check your division's policy for the care of plants and animals and observe the following general considerations:

- Do not use live vertebrate animals for experimental purposes (for experimenting with living conditions or food requirements).
- Keep living things in containers or facilities that ensure their safety and students' safety.
- Do not keep wild vertebrates, turtles, or birds (or bird's nests) in the classroom, as they may transmit disease.
- Ensure that students always wash their hands thoroughly after handling plants, animals, soil, or chemicals.
- Have students wear disposable gloves when cleaning animal cages.
- Invertebrates such as mealworms, earthworms, and caterpillars are ideal for classroom use because they do not transmit disease and are easily acquired. Have students practise respect for living things and the environment by returning the invertebrates to their habitat when the investigation is complete.
- When purchasing classroom pets, ensure you are buying them from a reputable dealer who will supply disease-free stock.

Respect for the Environment

When you conduct a field trip and observe or collect materials outdoors, you are a role model for students. You can model respect for the environment in the following ways:

- Collect samples from places that are public property, or obtain permission to remove samples from private property.
- Put objects such as rocks and soil back where they were collected when the investigation is complete.
- If possible, draw pictures and take photographs of animals, insects, and plants rather than bringing them back to class.
- If the above is not possible, collect samples of plants, animals, and insects in ways that do not harm them.
- Return animals and insects to their habitats as soon as possible.
- Ensure the areas you visit are cleaner when you leave than when you arrived. Leave only your footsteps.
- Reuse, reduce, and recycle materials in your classroom.

Pearson Science 6–8
Teacher's Resource — Generic Line Masters

Assessment Rubrics

Learning Contexts

Inquiry Skills

Skills Worksheets

Inquiry Skills

Data Analysis

Literacy Strategies

Name: ______________________

Scientific Inquiry

	Level 1	Level 2	Level 3	Level 4
Knowledge				
Understanding of Concepts	Student demonstrates limited understanding of science concepts related to the topic.	Student demonstrates some understanding of science concepts related to the topic.	Student demonstrates considerable understanding of science concepts related to the topic.	Student demonstrates thorough understanding of science concepts related to the topic.
Skills				
Initiating and Planning • Posing questions • Designing inquiry	Student inquiry plans show little relationship to the question or problem.	Student question and inquiry plans relate to the problem but may not be testable.	Student poses testable question and hypothesis related to inquiry topic; materials and procedure relate to the question.	Student inquiry plans include a testable question and hypothesis, materials, a sequential procedure, and possible relationships among variables.
Performing and Recording • Data collecting • Data recording	Student follows procedure, collects limited data, and does not record information in an organized manner.	Student uses equipment effectively, follows the procedure, collects data, and records information in an organized manner (using tables, numbers, etc., when possible).	Student uses equipment effectively and completes the investigation as planned with ease; measures and records data in an organized manner (using tables, numbers, and SI units (where applicable)).	Student manipulates scientific instruments effectively and appropriately for the investigation, records data in an organized manner (using tables, numbers, SI units), and makes notes about other evidence (where possible).
Analyzing and Interpreting • Identifying patterns in data • Graphing • Proposing explanations	Student organizes data collected but it is not in a form that can be easily interpreted or evaluated.	Student organizes data so that it can be interpreted or evaluated.	Student organizes data so that it can be interpreted or evaluated and completes some interpretation or evaluation.	Student organizes data so that it can be interpreted or evaluated and applies the results of the interpretation or evaluation.
Communication and Teamwork • Stating conclusion • Sharing results	Student reaches a simple conclusion and creates a basic written or oral report to communicate results.	Student reaches a conclusion based on findings and uses neatly written or oral report to communicate results.	Student reaches a conclusion based on findings and consistent with purpose and uses well-structured written or oral report to communicate results.	Student uses exemplary written or oral skills and techniques to communicate conclusion in a manner appropriate to audience.

	Level 1	Level 2	Level 3	Level 4
STSE				
Nature of Science and Technology	Student demonstrates little recognition that science knowledge results from systematic testing of ideas.	Student demonstrates some recognition that science knowledge results from systematic testing of ideas.	Student demonstrates considerable recognition that science knowledge results from systematic testing of ideas.	Student demonstrates a high degree of recognition that science knowledge results from systematic testing of ideas.
Social and Environmental Contexts of Science and Technology	Student shows little understanding of the social and environmental connections to science and technology.	Student shows some social and environmental connections to the inquiry.	Student includes social connections and environmental considerations in communicating the results of the inquiry.	Student includes social connections and environmental considerations and recognizes the need for peer acceptance of findings.
Attitudes				
Interest in Science • Obtaining hands-on experience • Observing during class and on field trips • Reading, watching, listening	Student demonstrates curiosity in the content area, in familiar contexts, with limited effectiveness.	Student demonstrates curiosity in the content area, in familiar contexts, with some effectiveness.	Student demonstrates curiosity in the content area, in familiar and unfamiliar contexts, with considerable effectiveness.	Student demonstrates curiosity in the content area, in familiar and unfamiliar contexts, with a high degree of effectiveness.
Inquiry in Science	Student shows little understanding of the need for evidence.	Student shows some understanding of the need for evidence relating to the hypothesis or purpose.	Student recognizes the need for evidence that either supports or refutes the hypothesis or purpose.	Student recognizes the need for accuracy, precision, and honesty in collecting relevant evidence to support or refute the hypothesis or purpose.
Collaboration • Co-operating with classmates	Student works in a group throughout the inquiry process.	Student contributes to group throughout the inquiry process.	Student contributes and listens to group throughout the inquiry process.	Student contributes to group and considers and builds on the contribution of other members throughout the inquiry process.
Safety • Considering self and other students • Considering plants and animals	Student demonstrates limited concern for safety with respect to self, other students, and/or live specimens.	Student demonstrates some concern for safety with respect to self, other students, and/or live specimens.	Student demonstrates concern for safety with respect to self, other students, and/or live specimens, including use of protective devices as appropriate.	Student demonstrates high degree of recognition of need for safety in planning and carrying out procedures for self, other students, and/or live specimens.

Name: ______________________

Technological Problem Solving

	Level 1	Level 2	Level 3	Level 4
Knowledge				
Understanding of Concepts	Student demonstrates limited understanding of the scientific principles and technological processes related to the problem.	Student demonstrates some understanding of the scientific principles and technological processes related to the problem.	Student demonstrates considerable understanding of the scientific principles and technological processes related to the problem.	Student demonstrates thorough understanding of the scientific principles and technological processes related to the problem.
Skills				
Initiating and Planning • Identifying a practical problem • Developing possible solutions	Student identifies a practical problem and comes up with a solution and procedure with assistance.	Student identifies a practical problem and identifies a single solution and procedure.	Student identifies a practical problem, generates several solutions, selects a solution, and develops a simple procedure.	Student identifies a practical problem, generates several solutions, selects a solution from several alternatives, and develops a detailed procedure.
Performing and Recording • Building a prototype • Carrying out plan of action	Student builds a prototype or carries out plan of action with assistance.	Student builds a prototype or carries out plan of action with limited effectiveness.	Student builds a prototype or carries out plan of action with considerable effectiveness.	Student builds a prototype or carries out plan of action with a high degree of effectiveness.
Analyzing and Interpreting • Testing the prototype/plan of action (if applicable)	Student tests the prototype/plan of action.	Student tests and evaluates whether the prototype/plan of action works.	Student determines modifications that can be made after the prototype/plan of action is tested.	Student makes modifications as a result of testing and then retests the improved prototype/plan of action.
Communication and Teamwork • Designing and developing the solution	Student contributes little to the team in development, testing, and evaluation of technological solution.	Student contributes to the team in development, testing, and evaluation of technological solution.	Student contributes effectively to the team in development, testing, and evaluation of technological solution.	Student contributes to the team and takes on a leadership role in development, testing, and evaluation of technological solution.

	Level 1	Level 2	Level 3	Level 4
STSE				
Nature of Science and Technology	Student does not distinguish between science and technology.	Student distinguishes between scientific ideas and technological solutions.	Student understands processes used in science and technology to develop technological solutions.	Student understands processes used in science and technology to understand natural phenomena and develop technological solutions.
Relationship between Science and Technology	Student expresses ideas for using technology to meet a human need.	Student ideas for using technology to meet a human need are based on science.	Student expresses the connection between science and technological problems.	Student shows sound understanding of the relationship between technological problems and their basis in science.
Social and Environmental Contexts	Student demonstrates limited understanding of the social and environmental implications of the technology.	Student demonstrates some understanding of the social and environmental implications of the technology.	Student demonstrates considerable understanding of the social and environmental implications of the technology.	Student demonstrates a high degree of understanding of the social and environmental implications of the technology.
Attitudes				
Collaboration • Co-operating with other students	Student works individually to solve problem.	Student collaborates with other students for portions of the problem-solving process.	Student collaborates effectively with other students for portions of the problem-solving process.	Student collaborates effectively with other students throughout all aspects of the problem-solving process.
Stewardship • Demonstrating the need for stewardship	Prototype development or plan of action shows limited understanding of the need for environmental stewardship.	Prototype development or plan of action shows some understanding of the need for environmental stewardship.	Prototype development or plan of action shows considerable understanding of the need for environmental stewardship.	Prototype development or plan of action shows significant understanding of the need for environmental stewardship.
Safety • Concerning self and others	Student demonstrates limited concern for safety of self and others.	Student demonstrates some concern for safety of self and others.	Student demonstrates considerable concern for safety of self and others.	Student demonstrates a high degree of concern for safety of self and others.

Name: ______________________

STSE Decision Making

	Level 1	Level 2	Level 3	Level 4
Knowledge				
Understanding of Concepts	Student shows limited understanding of the science, technology, societal, and environmental concepts related to the issue.	Student shows some understanding of the science, technology, societal, and environmental concepts related to the issue.	Student shows considerable understanding of the science, technology, societal, and environmental concepts related to the issue.	Student shows thorough understanding of the science, technology, societal, and environmental concepts related to the issue.
Skills				
Initiating and Planning • Identifying an issue • Planning research	Student struggles to recognize an issue and propose a solution.	Student clearly identifies an issue and proposes a solution.	Student clarifies an issue and develops a plan to proceed.	Student clarifies an issue and develops a plan, considering STSE implications.
Performing and Recording • Identifying stakeholders • Acquiring and evaluating information	Student researches and documents some information related to issue.	Student researches and documents information related to issue, recognizing different points of view.	Student researches and documents information from several different sources, recognizing points of view of different stakeholders.	Student researches and documents information from different sources, considering bias and recognizing points of view of different stakeholders.
Analyzing and Interpreting • Generating courses of action • Creating a plan • Assessing impact of action	Student chooses a course of action.	Student chooses a course of action from a list of possibilities generated.	Student evaluates pros and cons of possible actions and chooses an action based on criteria.	Student evaluates actions, identifies values with each possible action, and then chooses a course of action based on criteria.
Communication and Teamwork • Implementing decision or plan of action • Reporting (oral or written)	Student reports on the decision or plan of action of the team.	Student communicates within the team and reports on the decision or plan of action of the team.	Student communicates within the team and reports on the decision or plan of action of the team with supporting research or analysis.	Student communicates effectively within the team and reports on the decision or plan of action of the team with supporting research, reflecting on the process.

	Level 1	Level 2	Level 3	Level 4
STSE				
Nature of Science and Technology	Student shows little understanding of the connections between societal issues and development of technologies and scientific knowledge.	Student recognizes that there are connections between societal issues and development of technologies and scientific knowledge.	Student makes connections between societal issues and development of technologies and scientific knowledge.	Student understands connections between societal issues and development of technologies and scientific knowledge.
Social and Environmental Contexts of Science and Technology	Student demonstrates some understanding of the importance of society and the environment in decision making related to issues.	Student recognizes that society and the environment must be considered in decision making related to issues.	Student takes social and environmental implications into consideration when making decisions related to issues.	Student makes informed decisions related to issues, taking into account environmental and societal advantages and disadvantages.
Attitudes				
Collaboration • Researching • Choosing alternatives • Implementing plan	Student works in a group.	Student contributes to group.	Student contributes and listens to group.	Student contributes to group and considers and builds on the contributions of other members.
Stewardship • Researching • Planning • Assessing • Reporting	Student demonstrates limited understanding of the implications of decisions in relation to society or the natural environment.	Student demonstrates some understanding of the implications of decisions in relation to society and the natural environment.	Student demonstrates responsibility to society and the natural environment in decision making.	Student considers responsibility to society and the natural environment in every step of the decision-making process.
Appreciation of Science • Understanding our world • Differing perspectives	Student considers only one perspective on an issue.	Student recognizes that there could be more than one perspective related to an issue.	Student takes different perspectives into consideration in the decision-making process.	Student understands how different perspectives help broaden science as a means of understanding the natural world.

Name: ______________________

Cultural Perspectives

	Level 1	Level 2	Level 3	Level 4
Knowledge				
Understanding Key Science Concepts	Student demonstrates limited understanding of science concepts related to the topic.	Student demonstrates some understanding of science concepts related to the topic.	Student demonstrates sound understanding of science concepts related to the topic.	Student demonstrates excellent understanding of science concepts related to the topic.
Understanding Key Cultural Knowledge	Student demonstrates limited understanding of Indigenous or other cultural knowledge related to the topic.	Student demonstrates some understanding of Indigenous or other cultural knowledge related to the topic.	Student demonstrates sound understanding of Indigenous or other cultural knowledge related to the topic.	Student demonstrates excellent understanding of Indigenous or other cultural knowledge related to the topic.
Skills				
Initiating and Planning • Posing questions • Planning investigations	Student approaches inquiry without understanding of Indigenous and other cultural perspectives.	Student recognizes that there are Indigenous or other cultural perspectives.	Student shows some consideration of Indigenous or other cultural perspectives.	Student considers holistic perspectives in planning an inquiry.
Performing and Recording • Conducting inquiries • Gathering and recording data	Student shows little interest in and respect for the natural world.	Student makes observations of the natural world.	Student documents observations of the natural world.	Student observes and documents the natural world holistically and with respect.
Analyzing and Interpreting • Analyzing data • Assessing explanations	Student only considers scientific methods of analyzing and interpreting data.	Student recognizes scientific and cultural methods of analyzing and interpreting data exist.	Student shows understanding that there are different ways of knowing the natural world.	Student considers or proposes explanations of natural phenomena based on traditional knowledge.
Communication and Teamwork	Student shows little recognition of oral traditions for communicating wisdom.	Student shows some recognition of oral traditions for communicating wisdom.	Student recognizes oral traditions for communicating wisdom.	Student chooses oral traditions for communicating wisdom.

	Level 1	Level 2	Level 3	Level 4
STSE				
Nature of Science and Technology	Student shows little understanding that there are both scientific and other cultural knowledge systems.	Student refers to scientific and other cultural knowledge systems.	Student recognizes both scientific and other cultural knowledge systems and technologies.	Student recognizes and respects both scientific and other cultural knowledge systems and technologies.
Social and Environmental Contexts of Science and Technology • Planning projects • Reporting findings	Student shows little understanding of cultural and environmental connections to science and technology.	Student shows some understanding of cultural and environmental connections to science and technology.	Student shows considerable understanding of cultural connections and environmental considerations to science and technology.	Student shows a high degree of respect for and understanding of cultural perspectives and environmental considerations to science and technology.
Attitudes				
Collaboration • Planning investigations • Conducting inquiries • Gathering data	Student recognizes that there are Knowledge Keepers.	Student recognizes that Knowledge Keepers may have traditional knowledge related to topic of inquiry.	Student recognizes that there are protocols for obtaining knowledge from Knowledge Keepers and sharing it with others.	Student honours protocols for obtaining knowledge from Knowledge Keepers and taking responsibility for knowing it.
Appreciation of Science • Planning projects • Reporting findings	Student shows little understanding of the contributions of people from various cultures to understanding natural phenomena.	Student shows some understanding of the contributions of people from various cultures to understanding natural phenomena.	Student recognizes the contributions of people from various cultures to understanding natural phenomena.	Student appreciates and values the contributions of people from various cultures to understanding natural phenomena.
Stewardship • Posing questions • Planning inquiries • Analyzing data	Student shows little recognition that there is place-based knowledge.	Student shows some recognition that there is place-based knowledge.	Student recognizes place-based knowledge.	Student values place-based knowledge to solve local problems.

Name: ______________________________

Initiating and Planning

	Level 1	Level 2	Level 3	Level 4
Initiating the Task				
Identifying Topic of Inquiry	Student is not able to identify a question, practical problem, or issue having societal or environmental implications related to the science topic being studied.	Student identifies, with assistance, a topic-related question to answer, a practical problem to solve, or an issue having societal or environmental implications.	Student identifies a topic-related question to answer, a practical problem to solve, or an issue having societal or environmental implications.	Student clearly identifies and refines a topic-related question to answer, a practical problem to solve, or an issue having societal or environmental implications.
Developing Background Knowledge				
Researching Inquiry Problem	Student researches information from one source.	Student researches from multiple sources of information related to the problem.	Student researches and evaluates multiple sources of information related to the problem.	Student researches and evaluates multiple sources of information related to the problem, considers different perspectives, and identifies bias in information.
Planning Inquiry				
Posing Question (if applicable)	Student poses a testable question.	Student poses a testable question and develops a working hypothesis.	Student poses a testable question, identifies variables, and develops a working hypothesis.	Student poses a testable question, identifies variables and possible relationships, and develops a working hypothesis.
Planning Procedures				
Creating Inquiry Plan	Student identifies some procedures to follow.	Student develops a written plan of procedures.	Student develops a written plan of procedures with most materials included.	Student understands the need for, and develops, a comprehensive written plan with detailed procedures, including materials, to safely guide the inquiry.

Name: ____________________

Performing and Recording

	Level 1	Level 2	Level 3	Level 4
Performing Inquiry				
Implementing Plan	Student implements a prescribed plan.	Student safely implements a prescribed plan.	Student safely implements his/her own written plan with guidance.	Student safely implements his/her own written plan independently.
Recording Data				
Gathering Evidence	Student collects data using a limited number of tools and techniques.	Student collects and records data safely using a limited number of tools and techniques.	Student collects and records data safely using various tools and techniques.	Student collects and records appropriate data safely using various tools and techniques.
Organizing Data				
Representing Evidence	Student reports data but format is not well organized and does not lend itself to analysis.	Student reports data using a simple data table.	Student organizes data in a form appropriate to the task.	Student organizes and displays data using various modes of representation appropriate to the task.
Refining Inquiry Plan				
Evaluating Plan	Student discusses inquiry plan, prototype construction, or options to develop plan of action.	Student considers inquiry plan, prototype construction, or options to develop plan of action.	Student assesses inquiry plan, prototype construction, or options to develop plan of action.	Student assesses and refines inquiry plan, prototype construction, or clarifies options to develop plan of action.

Name: ______________________________

Analyzing and Interpreting

	Level 1	Level 2	Level 3	Level 4
Analyzing Data				
Assessing Evidence	Student identifies some patterns in the data.	Student identifies most patterns or relationships within the data.	Student identifies patterns and relationships within the data that relate to problem, prototype, or issue.	Student identifies patterns and relationships in the data and correctly relates them to problem, prototype, or issue.
Understanding Need for Evidence	Student does not recognize that knowledge in science is based on evidence.	Student recognizes that evidence is needed to develop knowledge in science.	Student understands the need for evidence to develop knowledge in science.	Student clearly understands the need for evidence, ideally quantitative, to develop knowledge in science.
Interpreting Data				
Proposing Explanations	Student attempts, but is unable, to explain patterns or relationships within the data.	Student proposes some explanations of patterns or relationships within the data.	Student proposes explanations of patterns and relationships within the data.	Student correctly proposes explanations of all relevant patterns and relationships within the data.
Refining Explanations	Student attempts a new prediction, suggests changes to prototype, or comments on a decision or plan of action.	Student makes new prediction but the connection to data is weak, suggests improvements to the prototype not based on evidence, or assesses the decision or plan of action.	Student makes new prediction based on data, suggests improvements to the prototype, or critically assesses the decision or plan of action.	Student makes an insightful prediction based on data, suggests effective improvements to the prototype, or assesses the decision or plan of action considering science concepts.
Considering Context	Student shows little recognition of the need to consider societal and environmental factors when interpreting and reporting on data.	Student recognizes the need to consider societal and environmental factors when interpreting and reporting on data.	Student understands the need to consider societal and environmental factors in proposing explanations, developing technologies, or recommending solutions.	Student understands and incorporates societal and environmental factors in proposing explanations, developing technologies, or recommending solutions.

Name: ____________________

Communication and Teamwork

	Level 1	Level 2	Level 3	Level 4
Communicating				
Expressing Ideas • Various forms of media: text, charts, diagrams, drama, debate	Student uses some conventions, vocabulary, and terminology in written communication of results.	Student uses conventions, vocabulary, and terminology in organized written or visual communication of results.	Student uses conventions, vocabulary, and terminology in various media, to communicate results.	Student effectively uses conventions, vocabulary, and terminology in various appropriate media, to communicate results.
Addressing Audience • Appropriate for target audience: written report, chart and diagram, oral or visual format	Student expresses and organizes ideas and information with limited effectiveness.	Student expresses and organizes ideas and information with some effectiveness.	Student expresses and organizes ideas and information taking audience or purpose into consideration.	Student effectively expresses and organizes ideas and information taking audience and purpose of project into consideration.
Teamwork				
Collaborating with Others	Student collaborates little with classmates throughout the inquiry.	Student collaborates occasionally with classmates and sometimes acknowledges the contributions of others.	Student collaborates with classmates throughout most of the inquiry, contributing effectively to the team and listening to the contributions of others.	Student collaborates with classmates through the entire inquiry process, contributing positively to the team and encouraging and respecting the contributions of others.
Reflection				
Reflecting on the Inquiry Process	Student shows little ability to reflect on the inquiry process and does not suggest ideas for improvement.	Student reflects on some aspects of the inquiry but does not suggest ideas for improvement.	Student reflects on most aspects of the inquiry and suggests few ideas for improvement.	Student reflects on all aspects of the inquiry, including the results obtained, and provides suggestions for improving the process.

Name: ______________________________

Inquiry Skills: Observing

Observing is using one or more of your senses to gather information about the world. Information gathered from observations is called evidence, or data. When you make observations in science, you want them to be accurate and objective. An *accurate* observation is an exact report of what your senses tell you. An *objective* observation avoids opinions, or bias, based on a specific point of view. *Quantitative* observations include numbers. *Qualitative* observations do not have numbers but include descriptions.

Hints for Making Observations

- **Be sure your observations are accurate and objective.**
- **You can record qualitative observations based on your sense of sight, hearing, touch, and/or smell. Safety First: NEVER taste any substance in the laboratory.**
- **When appropriate, count or use instruments to make quantitative observations. Always include units, for example, for a mass measurement of 5 g or a distance measurement of 15 m.**
- **If no measuring instruments are available, estimate by using known standards. For example, an object is about as long as a new pencil or has about the mass of a paper clip.**

Practise Your Observing Skills

Put a checkmark beside the observations you think are **accurate**.

Underline any that are **objective**.

Circle any that are **quantitative**.

Put a box around any that are **qualitative**.

Explain how you made these decisions.

1. One student recorded: "Sixteen students were present for attendance, and five other students arrived afterward."

continued ➡

2. Another student recorded: "Half the class was late."

3. A third student recorded: "The friendliest people were there first."

4. One visitor to the classroom wrote: "The classroom walls are yellow."

5. Another visitor noted: "The teacher's desk is about as long as an adult's bicycle."

6. A third visitor wrote: "The chalkboard is 1 m high and 2 m wide."

Name: ____________________

Inquiry Skills: Measuring

Measurements are important in science because they provide specific information and help observers avoid bias. Measuring is comparing an object or process to a standard. There are two things to watch carefully in measuring: choosing the right standard or unit, and performing the measurement itself.

Hints for Making Measurements

- **Know the purpose of your measurement. Choose the most suitable unit: for example, centimetres for a book or metres for the classroom floor.**
- **Know how your measuring tool works: for example, what main units it measures and what the smaller units mean.**
- **Always label your measurements. If you perform any math operations, such as adding or subtracting measurements, always label the resulting numbers properly.**
- **Determine whether you will need one, two, or a series of measurements. For example, if you need to find a change in temperature, you will need to subtract the original temperature from the final temperature.**
- **Know any special rules that apply. If you aren't sure, ask. For example, read the water level in a graduated cylinder at eye level and at the lowest point of the curved surface.**

Practise Your Measuring Skills

1. You have a centimetre ruler, a metre ruler, a graduated cylinder, and a balance. Which tool would you use to measure each of the following? Why? What unit would your measurement have?
   - the amount of juice in a drinking box
   - the size of a drinking box
   - a table
   - the load in your backpack

continued ➡

2. Use the appropriate ruler to measure the length of your arm. Express this length in millimetres, centimetres, metres, and kilometres. Which unit would you use to compare your arm's length to the length of your leg? Which unit would you use to compare your arm's length to the length of the classroom floor?

3. Make your own device to measure the volume of your hand, wrist, and arm as accurately as possible. Use your device to obtain data on the volume of each arm for left- and right-handed individuals. Do you find any pattern? What other questions could your measurements help answer?

Name: ______________________

Inquiry Skills: Classifying

Classifying is organizing objects and events into groups according to a system or organizing idea. The simplest type of classification system uses two groups, one that has a certain property and another that does not. Other systems may begin with three or more groups. Scientists choose the system that best suits their purpose. They may classify to organize objects such as the chemicals stored in a laboratory. They also classify to help simplify and make sense of the natural world. Good classification systems make finding information easier. They also help to clarify the relationships among the things being classified.

Hints for Classifying

- **Carefully observe the group of objects to be classified. Identify similarities and differences among the objects.**
- **Choose a characteristic that some of the objects share. Using this characteristic as the organizing idea, place the objects into groups.**
- **Examine the groups and decide if they can be further classified. Each round of further classification may need a different organizing idea.**

Practise Your Classifying Skills

1. Write down everything that you used in some way since waking up this morning until arriving at school. Choose a system or organizing idea to classify this list into two groups. Explain your reasoning.

continued ➡

2. Consider your two groups. How could you further classify these items? If you wish, continue until you have small groups that contain only very similar items.

3. Compare your classification system with that of another student. Make any modifications you wish.

4. Use your classification system to answer these questions:
   - What do I use that I have only at home?
   - If I travel away from home, what would I need to take with me to get ready for the day?
   - How would a power failure affect my morning routine?
   - How many other people are involved in getting me to school each day?

Name: ______________________

Inquiry Skills: Predicting and Hypothesizing

When you develop a hypothesis, you are making a prediction about the outcome of a scientific investigation based on your past experiences or the current evidence available. One of the most common methods of developing hypotheses is to look for a pattern. When you develop a hypothesis in science, you need to be as specific as possible. In science, hypotheses must be testable. This means that researchers should be able to carry out an investigation and obtain evidence that shows whether the hypothesis is true or false.

Hints for Developing Hypotheses

- **Don't just guess. When developing a hypothesis, examine all the evidence available to you.**
- **Look for a pattern in the evidence you are examining.**
- **Make sure the hypothesis is a prediction.**
- **Make sure the hypothesis can be tested through observations.**
- **Check the way you worded the hypothesis. A properly worded hypothesis should take the form of an "If ... then ..." statement.**
- **Don't be disappointed if your hypothesis turns out to be false. Whether right or wrong, a hypothesis may lead you to new questions and new hypotheses.**

Practise Your Hypothesizing Skills

1. Read the following hypotheses. Put a checkmark beside those containing testable predictions. Circle any hypothesis that is not properly worded, and rewrite that hypothesis.

   - If I give my plants fertilizer, then they will grow as big as my neighbour's plants.

   - If I get lucky, then my plants will grow bigger.

   - My plants aren't growing bigger because I don't water them enough.

continued ➡

2. Write a properly worded hypothesis based on this question: "Will empty trucks use the same amount of gasoline as heavily loaded trucks?"

3. Teachers often mention that good study habits will help improve any student's performance on a test. What are these habits? How could you find out the best ones for you to use? Find out about different study habits. Write a properly worded hypothesis for each habit that will help you find out which ones could help you in class.

Name: ____________________

Inquiry Skills: Posing Questions

Posing questions is an essential part of science. Scientific questions can be answered by observations or evidence. This is an important difference from other types of questions.

Hints for Posing Questions Related to Scientific Inquiry

- **Start by making a list of several questions related to the natural world.**
- **Review your list. If any questions cannot be answered by gathering evidence, delete them.**
- **If your questions are general, break them down into questions that can be investigated one at a time.**
- **Good questions that can be answered by scientific inquiry begin with:**
  "What is the relationship between …?"
  "What factors cause …?"
  "What is the effect …?"
- **Your questions should identify a relationship or factor you can investigate.**

Practise Your Questioning Skills

Directions: Read each statement below and indicate if it can be investigated scientifically or not. For statements that can be investigated, write a scientific question you would try to answer.

1. Animals at the top of the food chain eat plants and animals at the bottom of the food chain.

2. Eating too much junk food is bad for you.

3. Wayne Gretzky is the best hockey player ever.

4. When you hear thunder, lightning and rain are soon to follow.

continued ➡

5. Reducing energy consumption is a good thing.

6. Bears hibernate through the winter.

7. A red sunrise means the weather will change.

8. Sunlight is made of seven colours.

9. Structures made of concrete are more stable than structures made of wood.

10. Horoscopes correctly predict your future.

Name: ______________________

Inquiry Skills: Controlling Variables

Every experiment involves several variables, or factors that can change. For example, consider this question: Will house plants grow faster if you make the room warmer? To answer this question, you decide to grow plants at different temperatures. The variable that you purposely change and test — the temperature of the room — is called the manipulated variable. The factor that may change as a result of the *manipulated variable* — how fast the plants grow — is called the *responding variable*. An experimental plan is not complete unless the experimenter controls all other variables. Controlling variables means keeping all conditions the same except for the manipulated variable. In an experiment on temperature and plant growth, for example, you have to control any other variables that might affect the growth rate. Such variables include the size of the container, the type of soil, the amount of water, the amount of light, and the use of fertilizer. In addition, you would need to use identical plants in the experiment.

Hints for Controlling Variables

- **Start by describing the question or process being investigated. Then, identify the manipulated variable and the responding variable in the investigation. Predict the kinds of results you might observe in the responding variable.**
- **Create a list of all of the other variables that might affect the responding variable.**
- **Consider whether you have forgotten any of the most common types of variables: time, temperature, length, width, height, mass, volume, number, and the kinds of substances being used in the experiment.**
- **Determine whether or not one of the objects or groups of objects will serve as the control.**

Practise Your Skills at Controlling Variables

1. You are planning an experiment to find out whether the rate at which water freezes depends on the shape of its container. Identify the manipulated variable and the responding variable. List the other variables you would control.

continued ➡

2. Researchers want to determine the best temperature for storing batteries. Describe a possible experiment and list the variables in that experiment. Identify which are the manipulated and the responding variables.

3. Your friend has to plan an experiment for a science fair. He asks for your help. His topic is "The Strongest Cloth for Backpacks." What variables must his experiment include? What variables must be controlled?

4. Suppose you wanted to compare two different stain removers to learn which one was better at removing food stains from clothing. In your test, what variables would you need to control?

Name: ______________________________

Inquiry Skills: Forming Operational Definitions

Suppose that your class and another class work together on an experiment to determine what kinds of balls roll the fastest. When the experiment is finished, you all want to compare your data, so you must all perform the experiment in the same way. This means that each time a team of students repeats the experiment, they have to use the same materials and procedure as every other team. They must also make their measurements in an identical manner. Scientists also repeat investigations — their own and those of other researchers — to be sure that specific data are reliable. To make such repetition possible, scientists use operational definitions. An *operational definition* is a statement that describes how a particular variable is to be measured, or how an object or condition is to be recognized. Operational definitions tell you what to do or what to observe. (The word *operational* means "describing what to do.") Operational definitions need to be clear and precise so that a reader knows exactly what to observe or measure.

Hints for Forming Operational Definitions

- **Look over the written plan for carrying out an investigation, or write up a plan.**
- **Identify and list any variables or terms that do not have a single, clear, obvious meaning.**
- **If there are several reasonable ways to make an observation or to perform an action, choose one that suits the purpose of the investigation.**
- **Write a clear, complete definition of what the researcher should do or measure. Check your definition by asking yourself: Will this definition tell another person what to observe or how to measure? If necessary, revise your definition before starting your investigation.**

Practise Your Operational Definitions

Write an operational definition for each of the following. A good operational definition tells a person clearly how to perform an observation or take a measurement. Exchange your definitions with a partner to test if you can each follow the other person's instructions. Make any changes necessary.

1. On a cold day, let the water in the pan freeze outdoors.

continued ➡

2. You will test these two fertilizers to determine which one helps plants grow faster.

3. Rearrange the list of zoo animals in order of their size, with the biggest ones first.

4. You want to find out which kind of ball rolls fastest.

5. When you finish working on an experiment, wash your hands thoroughly.

Name: ______________________________

Data Analysis: Inferring

Making an inference, or inferring, is explaining or interpreting an observation or statement. Have you ever come home, smelled fish cooking, and thought, "We're having fish for dinner"? You made an observation using your sense of smell and used past experience to conclude what your next meal would be. Such a conclusion is called an inference. Inferences can be reasonable (logical) or unreasonable. A *reasonable inference* is one that makes sense, given what a person knows about the topic. One way to make an *unreasonable inference* is to conclude too much from the evidence.

When you are doing a scientific inquiry, you make observations and measurements. These recorded values are called your *data*. Once your data are collected, you need to interpret them. Interpreting data means looking for a pattern or trend. Data can be qualitative or quantitative. One way to find patterns in quantitative data is by graphing it. By analyzing your graph, you can determine if a pattern exists. Comparing your interpretation to something you already know will help you figure out if you have made a logical interpretation or a reasonable inference.

Hints for Inferring

- **Base your inference on accurate qualitative or quantitative observations.**
- **Organize your data into a table or arrange your data in some type of order.**
- **If your data is quantitative, you might make a graph for your data and then review your graph for patterns or trends.**
- **Using your data, infer what you think may be happening and compare your inferences with what you already know or have researched.**
- **Combine your observations with knowledge or experience to make an inference.**
- **Try to make more than one logical inference from the same observation.**
- **Evaluate the inferences. Decide what new information you need in order to show whether your inferences are true. If necessary, gather more information.**
- **Be prepared to modify, reject, or revise your inferences. A reasonable inference should make sense with everything else you know.**

continued ➡

Practise Your Inferring Skills

Part A: Qualitative Data

Suppose you are hiking on the prairie. You use binoculars and see a scene in which a few pronghorn antelope are standing near a herd of cattle. Some people in your group make the following observations and inferences. Which inferences are reasonable?

Observation: The cattle and the antelope are standing quietly together.
1. Inference: The cattle and antelope do not attack each other.
2. Inference: None of the animals in this region attack each other.

Observation: Some of the cattle are eating grass.
3. Inference: The grass is food for the cattle and antelope.
4. Inference: Most of the grass in this area is eaten by the cattle.

Observation: The antelope are looking around.
5. Inference: The antelope are watching for predators.
6. Inference: The antelope can see you.

Part B: Quantitative Data

One way to increase your interpreting skills is to think about the patterns shown on graphs instead of the data itself. Here's how: On a separate piece of paper, sketch a graph to show each of the following patterns. You won't be able to put in actual data, but you can label the axes and give the graph a title. You will also be able to draw in a line to show what is happening.

1. The height of a corn plant increases with time.

2. The number of cats found in an area increases just after the number of mice increases. The number of cats decreases after the number of mice decreases. This continues every year for ten years. (Hint: You may need two lines on the same graph.)

3. Using a bar graph, show a comparison between: (a) the approximate number of hours a week you spend on homework now, and (b) the number of hours a week you predict you will be spending on homework next year.

Name: ___________________________

Data Analysis: Graphing Data

Graphing is an important way to organize and present results in science. A graph lets you see patterns and trends that are very difficult to spot from a table of numbers. There are several types of graphs you can use, from bar to line to circle, and specialized types of graphs, such as best-fit line, and scatter plots. Be sure you are comfortable with all of these, because they will be very helpful as you interpret the results of your experiments.

Hints for Graphing Data

- **Start by organizing your data in a table. A table makes it easier for you to construct a graph.**
- **Give your graph a title that identifies the variables or the relationship between the variables in the graph. For example, "Number of Frog Croaks at Different Temperatures" is a complete title that clearly describes a graph.**
- **On graph paper, draw a horizontal, or *x*-, axis and a vertical, or *y*-, axis.**
- **Label the *x*-axis with the name of the manipulated variable (what you are studying). Label the *y*-axis with the name of the responding variable (measurements you have made). Include the units of measure.**
- **Determine the scale for the measurements to be shown on the vertical axis. Choose a scale that lets you represent all the values in your data table on the same page. Each square on the graph paper will represent a certain amount. All squares have the same value.**
- **If making a bar graph: on the *x*-axis, show a bar for each category being represented. Using your data, draw in the bars. Remember, all the bars must be the same width. Use an equal number of squares for the width of each bar and leave a space of at least one square between the bars.**
- **If making a line graph: plot each point where the variables intersect. You can do this by following an imaginary line up from the measurement on the *x*-axis. Then follow a second imaginary line across from the corresponding measurement on the *y*-axis. Place a dot where the two lines intersect.**
- **Consider whether you will plot from point to point or make a best-fit line graph. If you plot from point to point, each segment connecting two adjacent points should be straight. If you make a best-fit line graph, the connecting line should be smooth.**

continued ➡

Practise Your Graphing Skills

Make your own personal reminder sheet about graphs. Include an example of each type, with labels. Make notes about when you would use each type. Add any helpful tips you learn. Keep your sheet handy until you are confident about graphing data.

Name: ______________________

Answers to Skills Worksheets

LM 1 Process Skills: Observing

1. accurate; objective; quantitative
2. inaccurate; objective; quantitative (if we know the total number of students)
3. inaccurate; not objective; qualitative
4. accurate; objective; qualitative
5. inaccurate (but useful); objective; quantitative (a reasonable estimate based on a standard)
6. accurate; objective; quantitative

LM 2 Process Skills: Measuring

1. juice – cylinder; volume; mL box – centimetre ruler; close in size to object; cm table – metre ruler; close in size to object; m load – balance; mass; kg
2. Answers will vary. Watch for decimal places and units. To compare to leg: centimetres; to compare to floor: metres.
3. Methods and answers will vary.

LM 3 Process Skills: Classifying

Answers will vary. Encourage students to try several systems to form their groupings until they find one that helps them answer the questions most readily.

LM 4 Inquiry Skills: Predicting and Hypothesizing

1. testable; not testable (luck can't be measured); testable, but rewrite as: If I water my plants regularly, they will grow bigger than plants I do not water regularly.

LM 5 Inquiry Skills: Posing Questions

1. Yes. Sample question: What living things are in the diet of a hawk?
2. Yes. Sample question: What is the relationship between good health and the amount of junk food consumed?
3. No, although it could be argued that the analysis of statistics could be used to support the statement. The criteria for "best" are likely too variable.
4. Yes. Sample question: How frequently is the sound of thunder followed by lightning and rain within 30 min?
5. No, unless the term "good thing" is more closely defined.
6. Yes. Sample question: What environmental conditions cause bears to hibernate?
7. Yes. Sample question: What is the relationship between the appearance of a red sunrise and the occurrence of changing weather that day?

continued ➡

8. Yes. Sample question: What are the components of visible sunlight?

9. Yes. Sample question: Which will be more stable of two identical structures, one of wood or one of concrete?

10. No. The prediction must be something that can be measured and verified.

LM 6 Inquiry Skills: Controlling Variables

1. mv: container shape; rv: time until water freezes; other variables should include: volume of water, initial temperature of the water, temperature outside the container, composition of container.

2. Answers will vary. mv: storage temperature; rv: charge left in battery after storage; variables to be controlled: time in storage, initial charge in batteries, method of testing charge, how batteries are handled.

3. mv: mass or load used to test cloth strength; rv: time until cloth rips; variables to be controlled: method of testing, treatment of cloth samples, size of cloth samples.

4. mv: various food stains; rv: amount of stain removal; variables to be controlled: type of fabric, amount and preparation of staining material, amount of stain remover used, time allowed for stain remover to act on stain.

LM 7 Inquiry Skills: Forming Operational Definitions

Answers will vary. Emphasize the importance of clear communication. Pair students who have written different statements and ask them to follow each other's directions.

LM 8 Data Analysis: Inferring

Part 1

1. reasonable

2. unreasonable, because you have no evidence about any other animals

3. reasonable

4. unreasonable, because you have no evidence about the amounts eaten

5. reasonable

6. reasonable

Part 2

Model one of these examples for students if you wish. They are sometimes loath to make a sketch of a graph, but this is an excellent tool to help them make the connection between what a graph shows and what it means. Emphasize the identification of variables and units, as well as shape.

LM 9 Data Analysis: Graphing Data

Students may feel they have a good understanding of when and how to use graphs, but often fail to remember important details when the next opportunity to graph data arises. A study sheet is a way to empower students' own learning and to reassure them that they will have the information they need at hand in the future.

Name: ______________________

K-W-L Strategy

Topic

Before Reading	After Reading the Heading & Visual Aids	After Reading
K	**W**	**L**
What do we already know?	What do we want to know?	What have we learned or still need to learn?

(adapted from Ogle, 1986)

Name: ______________________

Predict-Read-Verify

Prediction: Subtitle ______________________ **page no.** __________

____

____

Prediction: True ☐ False/Incomplete ☐

If prediction was true — verify or give evidence to support it.
If prediction was false or incomplete — revise prediction below.

____

____

Prediction: Subtitle ______________________ **page no.** __________

____

____

Prediction: True ☐ False/Incomplete ☐

If prediction was true — verify or give evidence to support it.
If prediction was false or incomplete — revise prediction below.

____

____

Name: ______________________________

Key Word Concept Map

Term

What is it?

Comparison Term

Reminds me of:

Illustration

Describe it?

Examples

(adapted from Schwartz & Raphael, 1985)

Name: ______________________________

Note Taking

Teacher directions:

Take time to help students understand the structure and organization of the text. Begin by modelling and co-operatively using note-taking organizers, first as a class activity and then with students working in pairs.

Using the Cornell column format

Questions generated from headings	Details answering questions found in text

Questions	Text notes	Class discussion

Name: ______________________________

Where Do I Find the Answer?

Teacher directions:

Take time to help students understand the structure and organization of the text. This strategy can be used as a reference guide to assist students as they answer questions.

Stage one: The teacher can identify the type of questions assigned, for example, a "right there" question (the answer is located in one place), a "think and search" question (students will need to look in several places in the text), or a question that requires students to use both the text and their own knowledge.

Stage two: Students identify where an answer can be found either in one location in the text, several locations, and/or by using prior knowledge. Gradually, students should be able to identify how they found the answer to a question.

Students should understand how this strategy helps them expand and elaborate on simple answers, and assist them in answering inferential questions.

Where do I find it?

QAR — Question–Answer Relationship

QAR — Question–Answer Relationship Strategy

▶ **Right There:**	The answer is in one place in the text.
▶ **Think and Search:**	The answer is located in several places in the text. Remember the important places to search and support your answers and combine the information.
▶ **Text and You:**	The answer is not in the text; the student must use the author's information and combine it with personal background knowledge.
▶ **In My Head:**	The student must evaluate the information and form an opinion using background knowledge only.

(adapted from Raphael, 1982)

Name: ______________________

GIST or Key Ideas

Summary of Ideas | **Get the GIST in 20 words**

Summary of Ideas | **Get the GIST in 20 Words**

Summary of Ideas | **Get the GIST in 20 Words**

Name: ____________________

Think, Pair, Share

My Response

My Partner's Response

Our Response

Name: ______________________

Elaborative Interrogation

Change a fact or statement into a "Why" question.

Fact or Statement:

Why Question:

Why Question:

Why Question:

Fact or Statement:

Why Question:

Why Question:

Why Question:

Why Question:

(adapted from Pressley & Woloshyn, 1992)

Name: ____________________

Semantic Maps for Organizing Information

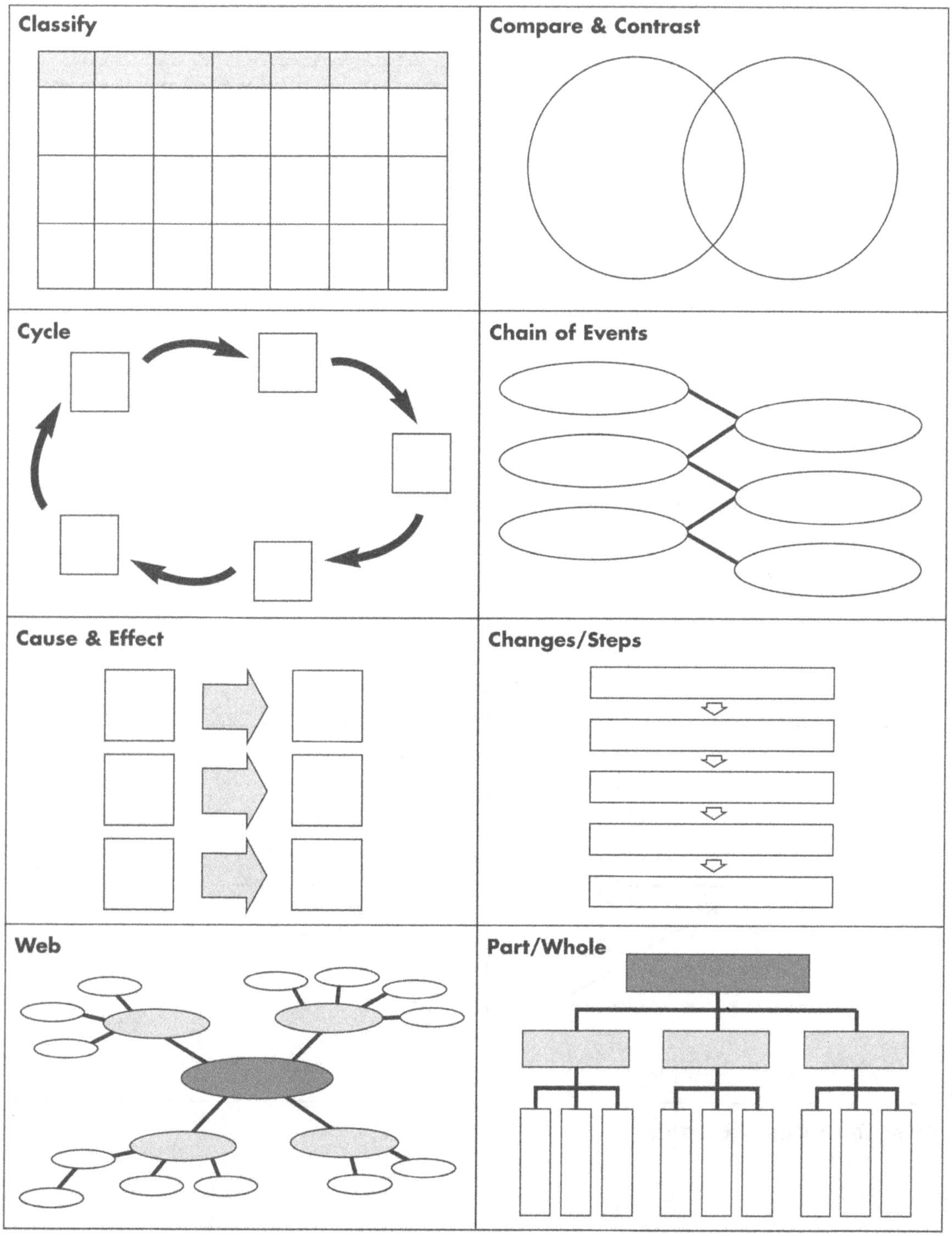

Name: ____________________

Reflect and Evaluate

Topic:

Interesting Information I Have Learned:	Why I Have Found This Information Interesting:

Directions for Future Learning:

continued ➡

Strategies for Enhancing Student Understanding of the Science Text

Students need guidance before, during, and after reading in order to assist them in understanding the text and constructing useful meanings for activities in science. Strategies and their purposes must be explicitly taught through teacher modelling and scaffolding until students can independently use them while reading. The following strategies are organized in three phases of guidance. These strategies can be grouped together for an activity or used at various stages during a lesson or unit. They can also be used as small- or large-group activities.

Before Reading Strategies to Enhance Student Understanding

Students need to recall prior knowledge and previous experiences, engage their curiosity, and make predictions before reading new text.

1. **K-W-L (Know, Want to Know, Learned Strategy)** (Ogle, 1986)
   K-W-L encourages students to become more involved in learning new concepts as it connects the new content to what students already know. It generates questions that can guide students and help them evaluate their learning. (See Literacy Strategies 1.)

2. **Predict-Read-Verify**
   Predict-Read-Verify helps students monitor their comprehension while interacting with the text. The teacher "chunks" the text into manageable sections for the students. Text material may be "chunked" by headings, paragraphs, or page numbers. Before reading, students are asked to read text headings, analyze visual aids, and read captions in each "chunk." Students use their background knowledge to predict what each "chunk" will be about. During the reading of the text, students will use the new textual information to verify or revise their predictions. (See Literacy Strategies 2.)

3. **Key Word Concept Maps** (adapted from Schwartz & Raphael, 1985)
   Key Word Concept Maps help students broaden their understanding of key word concepts. Before reading, new words and concepts can be pre-taught or clarified. During reading, they can be linked to the text. After reading, students can identify word concepts they wish to learn more about. (See Literacy Strategies 3.)

During Reading Strategies to Enhance Student Understanding

Students need to confirm and adjust previous predictions, relate new information to prior knowledge, draw conclusions, examine and possibly revise thinking, and make new predictions.

4. **Note Taking** (Cornell Format)
   Note taking helps students attend to and recall text information. Students rewrite topic headings in the form of questions (how? what? why?). As they read, they look for answers to these questions. Answers are recorded in the two-column or three-column note outlines. (See Literacy Strategies 4.)

continued ➡

5. **Where Do I Find the Answer? QAR — Question–Answer Relationship Strategy** (Raphael, 1982)
QAR teaches students to recognize that there are different ways of locating information for answering questions. Students must learn to categorize questions in order to answer them with more depth. A framework of four categories of questions is provided to guide students. (See Literacy Strategies 5.)

6. **GIST**
GIST helps students distil text material into its most important ideas or concepts. Students initially read a small portion of text (3–5 paragraphs), and write down the summary of ideas. They must reduce the passage to just twenty words that capture the gist of the text. Students must connect, analyze, and summarize facts and details in the text in order to reduce the text to a few key ideas. (See Literacy Strategies 6.)

7. **Think, Pair, Share**
Think, Pair, Share helps students confirm, expand, and refine their ideas by sharing responses with a partner. Students are asked to read a section of text independently, record their thoughts, and then pair with another student to discuss and share their thoughts on the text. Teachers may be explicit about the type of response students must provide. Partners collaborate to come up with one shared response. (See Literacy Strategies 7.)

8. **Elaborative Interrogation** (Pressley & Woloshyn, 1992)
Elaborative Interrogation helps students integrate their background knowledge with new information by generating and answering a "why?" question. Answering "why?" questions can facilitate the acquisition of new factual information. Students are required to take science facts and generate "why?" questions about them. For example: "Not all plants have roots." "Why don't all plants have roots?" or "Why don't all plants need roots?" (See Literacy Strategies 8.)

After Reading Strategies to Enhance Student Understanding

Students need to organize information after reading and respond to the text in some important way. This may involve identifying major concepts and ideas, perceiving relationships between concepts and ideas, perceiving relationships with prior knowledge, and understanding the relative importance of ideas.

9. **Semantic Mapping**
Semantic Mapping helps students actively think about textual information as they show relationships between new and known information. This strategy also helps students organize and recall text information. Semantic maps may demonstrate the flow or sequence of events, may compare and contrast, or show cause and effect, webbing, classification, descriptions, cycles, and part/whole relationships. (See Literacy Strategies 9.)

10. **Reflect and Evaluate**
It is important for students to reflect and evaluate their learning. In Reflect and Evaluate, students outline the interesting information they have learned and why they found it interesting. Students can use this as a springboard for directions in future learning, such as research projects. (See Literacy Strategies 10.)